MINISTRY OF
AGRICULTURE, FISHERIES AND FOOD

LAND DRAINAGE SERVICE

Water for Irrigation
Supply and Storage

Bulletin No. 202

GW00729952

LONDON
HER MAJESTY'S STATIONERY OFFICE

ISBN 0 11 241519 9

Contents

	Page
INTRODUCTION	1
ESTIMATION OF WATER REQUIREMENTS	
Crops and areas	3
Daily and hourly demand	3
Seasonal demand	4
Design year	4
Storage	5
WATER SOURCES	
Using water sources for irrigation . . .	6
Quantity of water available	6
Quality of the water	6
Cost of using the water	7
Abstraction licences	7
Impounding licences	8
Authority to test pump underground sources .	8
Abstraction licences and storage . . .	8
Surface water	8
Estimation of water available . . .	9
Methods of flow gauging	10
Field drainage	11
Ground water	11
Occurrence	11
Ground water abstraction	11
Yield	12
Public supply	12
STORAGE OF WATER	
The need for storage	13
Types of reservoirs	13
Storage of surface water	13
Storage of field drainage water . . .	13
Storage of ground water	14
Existing storage	14
Small reservoirs	14
Storage capacity	14
Nett storage capacity	15
Actual storage capacity	15
SELECTION OF SITES FOR EARTH RESERVOIRS	
Offstream reservoirs	16
Site location	16
Water to earth ratio	17
Impounding reservoirs	17

Page

Site location 17
Provision for spillway 18
Water to earth ratio 18
Site investigation 18
Trial holes 18
Existing field drains 19

DESIGN OF EARTH RESERVOIRS
Offstream reservoirs 20
Reservoir capacity and dimensions . . 20
Gravity supply 21
Feeder channel or pipe 21
Pumped supply 22
Pumping costs 22
Pump selection 22
Pump and delivery pipe 24
Overflow arrangements 24
Stream control weirs 25
Impounding reservoirs 25
The dam 25
Reservoir capacity and dimensions . . 25
Overflows 26
Overflow arrangement and design . . 27
Primary overflow capacity . . . 27
Primary overflow arrangement . . . 27
Spillway or storm overflow . . . 30
Design storm flow 30
Size of spillway channel 30
Spillway arrangement 30
Protection of spillway against erosion . . 33
Bottom outlet pipe 33
Bottom outlet bay 34
Seepage reservoirs 34
Water available 34
Need for seepage reservoirs . . . 34
Yield testing 35

DESIGN AND CONSTRUCTION OF EARTH EMBANKMENTS AND
DAMS
General principles 36
Foundations 36
Stability 36
Seepage control 37
Site preparation 37
Bottom outlet pipe 37
Embankments 38
Suitable soils 38
Soil testing 38
Types of construction 38

Homogeneous construction . . . 40
Zoned and diaphragm construction . . 40
Blanket construction 40
Method of constructing embankments . 44
Shapes and slopes of embankments
and excavations 44
Embankment protection 45
Reservoir pipework 45
Maintenance 47

WATERTIGHTNESS AND WATERPROOFING OF RESERVOIRS
The need for watertightness 48
Waterproofing methods 48
Sheet lining methods 48
Laying sheet linings 48
PVC sheet lining 49
Polyethylene sheet lining 50
Butyl rubber sheet lining 50
Soil treatment methods 50
Clay lining 50
Cut-off methods 51

APPENDICES

A   Bases for the design of a typical irrigation scheme . 52
B   Water quality 59
C   Capital costs of source works 61
D   90° vee notch flow gauge 64
E   Rectangular weir flow gauge 66
F   Winter flow gauge readings for a typical stream . 68
G   Estimation of stream flow in a dry winter . . 70
H   Calculation of storage capacity . . . 72
J   Water Authorities: addresses and telephone num-
bers 77
K   Offstream reservoirs: dimensions . . . 79
L   Impounding reservoirs: dimensions . . . 84
M   Offstream reservoirs: typical arrangements . 87
N   Impounding reservoirs: typical arrangements . 91
O   Report form for yield testing seepage reservoirs . 95
P   Metric units and conversions 96

LIST OF FIGURES

		Page
Fig. 1	Primary overflow arrangement . . .	29
Fig. 2	Spillway capacity (design storm flow) .	31
Fig. 3	Size of spillway channel	32
Fig. 4	Example of a typical soil test . . .	39
Fig. 5	Embankment construction: homogeneous construction	41
Fig. 6	Embankment construction: zoned construction	42
Fig. 7	Embankment construction: diaphragm construction	43
Fig. 8	Embankment construction: blanket construction	43
Fig. 9a and 9b	Bases for the design of a typical irrigation scheme . . . . . 58 and 59
Fig. 10	Installation of a 90° vee notch flow gauge .	65
Fig. 11	Installation of a rectangular weir flow gauge .	67
Fig. 12a to 12e	Nett short-term storage capacity . 72 and 73
Fig. 13	Map showing Water Authority areas .	78
Fig. 14	Offstream reservoir: capacity and depth of water	80
Fig. 15	Offstream reservoir: average depth of balanced excavation	82
Fig. 16	Offstream reservoir: water to earth ratio .	83
Fig. 17	Impounding reservoir: capacity and maximum depth of water	85
Fig. 18	Impounding reservoir: water to earth ratio	86
Fig. 19	Offstream reservoir: general arrangement for gravity filling	87
Fig. 20	Offstream reservoir: general arrangement for pump filling	88
Fig. 21	Offstream reservoir: typical inlet arrangement for gravity feed	89
Fig. 22	Offstream reservoir: typical inlet arrangement for pump feed	90
Fig. 23	Impounding reservoir: typical dam and spillway construction	91
Fig. 24	Impounding reservoir: bottom outlet pipe and combined primary overflow . .	92
Fig. 25	Impounding reservoir: typical construction of separate primary overflow . .	93
Fig. 26	Impounding reservoir: suggested design and construction of bottom outlet bay . .	94

LIST OF TABLES

		Page
Table 1	Examples of winter runoff . . .	10
Table 2	Maximum feeder channel velocities and slopes	21
Table 3	Friction losses in smooth pipes . . .	23
Table 4	Primary overflow sizes	28
Table 5	Cost of waterproofing earth reservoirs . .	50
Table 6	90° vee notch flow gauge: head and flow readings	64
Table 7	Rectangular weir flow gauge: head and flow readings	66
Table 8	Winter flow gauge readings for a typical stream	69

Foreword

FREQUENTLY the best and most economical solution to the problem of finding sufficient water for irrigation is to store it on the farm. Nearly one thousand farm storage reservoirs have already been constructed, and if development of irrigation is to proceed the number will need to increase significantly.

The complexity of soils and of geology, the highly organized layouts of our farms, the necessity to use all agricultural land to the utmost advantage, the close proximity to many farms of other development and the need to use water wisely all mean that the consideration of an irrigation storage project in this country can be a highly complex matter.

The purpose of this Bulletin, which has been prepared by Ministry Engineers who have been dealing with irrigation water supply problems over a long period, is to give guidance to all concerned with these matters and especially the design, construction or use of farm water storage, by gathering together the necessary information in a concise publication. It is not intended as a basis for 'do-it-yourself' techniques, the application of which are extremely limited in this context.

The Bulletin necessarily makes reference to other official publications which deal at greater length with particular aspects of irrigation. It does not take the place of more comprehensive specialist publications dealing with dam design, hydrology, etc., but, within the limitations of the normal farm scale of irrigation, it does provide suitable data and methods.

This is the second edition, which has been metricated and revised.

G. COLE
Chief Engineer

Ministry of Agriculture, Fisheries and Food
September 1976

Introduction

THE expansion of irrigation by spraying methods in the British Isles, particularly in the east of England, is one of the many developments in agriculture since the Second World War and in 1976 about 6000 agricultural holdings are equipped for irrigation. In drier parts of the world the role of irrigation is of great importance and, without it, in many areas crop growth would not be possible. In Britain, where most crops in most years can be grown relying on rainfall alone, irrigation is supplemental to rainfall and its object is to raise crop yields by avoiding the periodic checks to growth caused by lack of soil moisture which occur in most years and especially in the drier ones.

Irrigation depends on water being available elsewhere whenever the soil moisture is insufficient to maintain crop growth due to lack of rain, e.g., from surface or underground sources, including the underdrainage of the holding itself; however, the availability of water from these sources tends to diminish as the need for irrigation increases, for both result from the excess of evaporation over rainfall during the growing season. This is particularly true for rivers and streams. The solution to this problem in most cases is to provide a reservoir so that water can be abstracted and stored when it is available, usually in winter, for use during the irrigation season. The natural storage provided by underground sources may also need supplemental artificial storage if the water-bearing strata are of insufficient capacity.

Under the 1963 Water Resources Act and 1973 Water Act the responsibility for the allocation of water from all sources for all purposes, with minor exceptions, rests with the 10 Regional Water Authorities in England and Wales. Before an irrigator can abstract water from a source as defined in the 1963 Act he must first obtain an abstraction licence from the appropriate authority. Under the 1963 Act a licence is also required before a dam, weir or other impounding works can be constructed on a watercourse.

The purpose of this Bulletin is to give guidance on possible sources of supply, methods of storing water and in particular the design and construction of small farm reservoirs. It is not intended to give advice on the design and construction of reservoirs with embankment heights exceeding 5 metres nor on the large reservoirs which are within the scope of the Reservoir (Safety Provisions) Act 1930.

This Act requires that a reservoir designed to hold or capable of holding more than 5 million gallons of water above the natural level of any part of the land adjoining the reservoir must be designed, constructed under the supervision of and inspected from time to time by a qualified civil engineer on one of the panels constituted under the Act.

The Reservoir (Safety Provisions) Act 1930 has been replaced by the Reservoirs Act 1975 but at the time of writing the 1975 Act has yet to be implemented. This Act substitutes a capacity of 25 000 cubic metres for the 5 million gallons in the 1930 Act and, amongst other things, requires that local authorities establish and maintain a register of reservoirs covered by this Act and that they ensure that those responsible for the reservoirs observe and comply with the requirements of the Act.

Although this Bulletin gives guidance on the design and construction of reservoirs outside the scope of the Acts but within the limits mentioned above, local conditions vary to such an extent that a reservoir project of any significance is essentially a matter which requires the services of a qualified civil engineer who has experience in this field. Planning consent may be required for farm reservoir construction and the local planning authority should be consulted before any work is started.

The consideration of any irrigation scheme must start with a definition of the agricultural objective, i.e., the crops and areas to be irrigated. An estimate of the amount of water needed to irrigate these crops can then be made. If a source of water can satisfy this demand either with or without storage, then the agricultural objective can be achieved. If sufficient water is not available then a reappraisal of the agricultral objective must be made.

Metric units are used in this Bulletin. Appendix P lists the principal units and the approximate conversions from imperial to metric.

Estimation of Water Requirements

A BRIEF description of the methods used for determining the water needs of crops is given below and illustrated by the analysis of a typical irrigation scheme in Appendix A. For further information the reader should consult the Ministry Bulletin No. 138, *Irrigation*, and advice can also be sought from the local ADAS adviser.

CROPS AND AREAS

Fundamental to the design of an irrigation system as a whole, including any storage required, is a definite decision regarding the crops and areas which are to be irrigated in the design year, so that the total water requirement in that year can then be determined. The maximum daily and hourly water requirements depend on the maximum area which must be kept irrigated; this will usually occur in the months of June and July when the potential transpiration of the crops is highest.

DAILY AND HOURLY DEMAND

The peak daily and hourly requirements are based on the rate at which irrigation must be applied to control the soil moisture deficit (SMD) caused by the potential evapotranspiration of the crop, which in parts of the country can rise to an average maximum of 80 to 100 mm of water over the months of June or July. For design purposes an average potential evapotranspiration of 25 mm in 10 days is usually adopted for midseason crops.

It is theoretically possible to cover the whole irrigated area with irrigation equipment at the same time. This would enable close controls of the SMD but could only be justified for very valuable crops, although increases in labour costs and crop values may change this.

In practice the area covered by the equipment is considerably less than the total irrigated area. Most crops can tolerate a SMD before there is a significant effect on growth and the maximum acceptable SMD depends upon the crop and the soil type. Typical maximum values for field crops are 25, 38 or 50 mm of water. As the average potential evapotranspiration of crops causing the SMD is 25 mm in 10 days in the summer months, it would take 10, 15 or 20 days respectively to increase the SMD to the above amounts from when the soil is at field capacity (zero SMD). Thus if sufficient water is applied at one setting of the equipment to reduce the SMD to zero then it would not be necessary to irrigate the same area again for a period of 10, 15 or 20 days. This period is known as the irrigation cycle and during the cycle the opportunity is taken to irrigate other parts of the total area on the other days of the cycle. Thus the equipment can be moved at successive settings across the total area over a period of days and by this means the area of the equipment required need only be a fraction of the total area. The area of equipment can be further reduced by moving the equipment a number of times on any one day of the cycle. The number of daily moves or settings depends upon the rate at which water can be applied by the equipment, the SMD to be satisfied at one setting and the number of hours worked in the day.

Taking a typical example, if a particular crop can tolerate a maximum SMD of 38 mm and equipment is available which can apply 5 mm of water in one hour, then it would take 7·5 hours to reduce the SMD to zero. In a 15 hour working day there would be two moves or settings of the equipment and as it would take an irrigation cycle of 15 days for the SMD to increase to 38 mm from zero, there would be a total of $2 \times 15 = 30$ settings of the equipment. Thus if the total area to be irrigated is say 10 hectares, the area of equipment required would be $10 \div 30 = 0·33$ hectares. The hourly demand in litres per second is determined by the rate of application and the area of equipment, and the daily demand in cubic metres per day is determined by the number of working hours in the day. This is further explained in Appendix A. Increasing the number of daily working hours by 50 per cent would reduce the area of equipment required in the above example to 0·22 hectares. This would reduce the hourly demand in proportion to the reduction in area but the daily demand would remain the same.

Although in practice the irrigation cycle is not continuous because of rest days this would usually not affect the hourly and daily demand. However, the planned maximum SMD may be exceeded by a small margin.

SEASONAL DEMAND

Estimation of the total water requirement over the irrigation season is not just an extension of the estimate of daily demand but an entirely separate calculation. The reason is that whereas the daily and hourly demands are based on the control of the SMD assuming that no rain occurs during the irrigation cycle, the seasonal demand takes account of the rain which falls during the summer months. The procedure is described fully in Bulletin 138 and further advice can be obtained from the local ADAS adviser. The first step is to decide on the period for each crop during which irrigation is required, i.e., the crop response period, and then to decide the SMD which the crop can accept without restriction of growth for the particular soil type. With this information the amount of irrigation required in the design year can then be determined.

DESIGN YEAR

The choice of design year should be based on a comparison of costs and benefits over a period of years. Data are readily available for a 20 year period which includes a range of wet and dry periods appropriate to the response period of any particular crop. Thus undue emphasis is not given to extremely dry summers.

As a general indication it is likely to be well worth providing for the maximum irrigation need in the driest year where high value crops are concerned, subject to the water being reliably available at the times when it is needed. Careful consideration is needed however in deciding the design year if the water has to be obtained from storage, especially if all the water required over the irrigation season must be stored for the irrigation of extensive areas of low value crops or grassland requiring large amounts of water. In these case it may not be justifiable to provide for the driest year and many schemes have been designed for the fifth driest year in 20 as a maximum.

Information on irrigation requirements for a particular crop response period and planned SMD in the driest and the fifth driest year in 20 years can be obtained from maps of long-term irrigation need, which are available to your local ADAS adviser.

STORAGE

There is little doubt that sources of water which can be used for direct abstraction in the summer months are becoming very scarce and have the real disadvantage that they can be subject to failure or restriction in times of drought. The winter storage of irrigation water in a reservoir can provide a considerable amount of protection against the failure of a supply, but the size of reservoir needed to store water for a whole seasons's supply is usually substantial and can be costly to construct.

By way of illustration the size of reservoir required for a scheme for the intensive irrigation of 10 hectares of grass in eastern England would be about 50 000 m³ assuming no summer rainfall, about 30 000 m³ for the driest year in 20 and about 25 000 m³ for the fifth driest year in 20. Assuming a cost of £0·3 per cubic metre of water stored for an excavated and embanked unlined reservoir the cost of construction to meet the irrigation demand in the driest year in 20 would be about £9000 and about £7500 for the fifth driest year.

Water Sources

THE sources of water which may be available on a farm can be divided into three categories:

Surface water

Ground water

Public supply

Surface water includes the flow of rivers and streams, water stored in ponds and lakes and water derived from the underdrainage of the farm itself. Ground water is any water that can be abstracted from below the water table by means of wells, boreholes and open excavations. Public supply is potable water taken direct from the distribution mains of the local Water Undertaking.

USING WATER SOURCES FOR IRRIGATION

The use of any water source as an irrigation supply depends upon three factors:

Quantity of water available

Quality of the water

Cost of using the water

QUANTITY OF WATER AVAILABLE

Whatever the quantity of water available from a source may be, a licence from the Water Authority is required before the water can be legally abstracted for spray irrigation. This applies to both surface and ground water. A licence is also needed before water can be stored in an impounding reservoir. This is further explained below.

A source will be adequate if the total amount of water available during the irrigation season exceeds that required. Storage, however, is necessary if at any time the flow of water available is less than the rate of demand.

QUALITY OF THE WATER

The quality of the water, bacteriologically and chemically, must be adequate for the purpose and professional advice must be sought before using suspect water. Surface water may be contaminated with sewage, whereas ground water may contain considerable quantities of dissolved salts which could be detrimental to plant growth. It is clearly undesirable, for instance, to use contaminated water on crops which are consumed raw. Detergents present in surface water can affect plant growth and soil moisture capacity, but with a few exceptions river waters generally have not yet been found to contain a sufficient concentration to cause damage, except perhaps in the removal of lubricating oils from the bearings to pumps and other machinery. Water taken from public supplies is satisfactory in all respects. Further information is given in Appendix B.

Cost of Using the Water

The cost of an irrigation scheme, including water charges, interest and depreciation on the capital cost of works to receive or store a supply, must be low enough so that when other costs of irrigation are added, including labour, extra labour as necessary and fuel, there is a prospect of a reasonable increase in income from the irrigated crops. Further information on costs is given in Appendix C.

ABSTRACTION LICENCES

Under the provisions of the Water Resources Act 1963, and the Water Resources (Licences) Regulation 1965, a licence must be obtained from the appropriate Water Authority before abstracting water from any lake or watercourse or underground source of supply for the purpose of spray irrigation or before an existing licenced abstraction can be increased. Whether a licence is granted will depend upon the Water Authority's consideration of the availability of water at a particular place.

The abstraction licence specifies the point of abstraction, the land on which the water is to be used, the purpose for which the water is to be used, i.e., spray irrigation, the quantity of water which can be abstracted during specified periods, usually daily or annually, the means of abstraction, e.g., pump, and the basis of measuring or assessing the amount of water actually abstracted.

A charge is levied by the Authority on the basis of the licensed quantities and at rates laid down in the Authority's charging scheme. The charge rate varies according to the locality, source and time of abstraction. Winter abstraction rates are lower in cost than summer rates. Typical rates in 1976 for a place in eastern England are 0·35p per cubic metre for winter abstraction from surface sources and 1·74p per cubic metre for summer abstraction. For a place in central England the corresponding rates are 0·13p and 0·5p per cubic metre. Thus the cost of abstracting water to meet an irrigation seasonal demand of, say, 16 000 cubic metres at 0·13p per cubic metre would be £21, a comparatively small sum.

In recognition of the fact that in some years it is not necessary to abstract the licenced quantities in full there is usually a two-part tariff arrangement for spray irrigators. In this a proportion of the charge rate (e.g., 25 per cent) is allocated to the licenced annual quantity and the remainder (e.g., 75 per cent) is allocated to the quantity of water actually abstracted during the year. This allows some saving in cost in wetter years.

An abstraction licence confers on a licensee a 'protected right' to the quantity of water authorized for abstraction. Thus Water Authorities have a statutory duty not to issue additional licences or take other action which could prejudice the availability of sufficient water to meet the requirements of the licences for the time being in force.

In the case of spray irrigators there is an important limitation to the degree of protection afforded by a licence. In the event of exceptional shortage of rain or other emergency, a Water Authority may serve notices reducing for a specified period the quantity of water that may be abstracted for the purposes of spray irrigation.

IMPOUNDING LICENCES

A licence is required before constructing or altering any works for impounding or diverting the flow in a watercourse. An impoundment includes the construction of a weir across the line of a watercourse to locally raise the water level so that water can be abstracted, by diversion or by pump, upstream of the weir. It also includes the construction of a dam on the line of the watercourse for the purpose of creating an impounding reservoir.

The licence specifies the place where the impounding can take place, the retention level of the impoundment or the maximum quantity of water which can be impounded, and the residual flow of water which must be maintained in the watercourse downstream of the impoundment at all times.

A licence to impound is not the same as a licence to abstract but where there is an intention to impound and abstract, a combined licence is normally issued.

AUTHORITY TO TEST PUMP UNDERGROUND SOURCES

Authority to test pump a well or borehole must be obtained from the Water Authority before work is started. An abstraction licence is required before the water is taken on a permanent basis.

ABSTRACTION LICENCES AND STORAGE

If a licence is obtained to abstract water from any source and that water is then stored in an offstream reservoir, then any subsequent abstraction from the reservoir is not subject to control, i.e., it can be used as and when needed. As water is usually abstracted during the winter months for storage in an offstream reservoir, the possibility of an imposed reduction in the licensed quantities by the Water Authority during the winter months is remote and the farmer is reasonably assured of an adequate supply.

In the case of water stored in an impounded reservoir the situation is different. The impounding licence permits the storage of a specified amount of water but as mentioned above this is not a licence to abstract water from the reservoir. Licenced abstraction from an impounding reservoir will take place in the summer months and thus it should be recognized that there could be a possibility of an imposed reduction in the licensed quantities. The water charge rate could be less than the summer rate to reflect the presence of storage.

SURFACE WATER

Surface water is present on most farms in one form or another. It may be a major river taking the drainage of thousands of square kilometres or, at the other extreme, just the underdrainage from the farm itself. In some cases there will be existing storage, either natural or artificial, in the form of lakes and ponds. Whilst only a comparatively small proportion of farms are in the fortunate position of having enough water available for irrigation by direct abstraction throughout the summer, there are many where the total annual flow is sufficient if winter storage is feasible and provided a licence is granted. An estimate of the surface water available must be made to see if the irrigation requirements can be fully met, bearing in mind any limitations imposed by the licence.

ESTIMATION OF WATER AVAILABLE

If the source is a river or large stream and there appears to be plenty of water available, then it is advisable to consult the appropriate Water Authority as to the amount of water actually available. For sources such as small streams, where little is likely to be known about the water available, it is necessary to estimate the flow as accurately as possible. Frequent flow gaugings are the best guide. The next best is an estimate based on the stream catchment area and likely runoff. An estimation of the flow which may be available from all possible sources should be made at the earliest opportunity so that, by the time the decisions have to be taken, the best information will be available.

To assess the amount of water available in a stream for direct abstraction during the summer months, it is essential that the stream is gauged in a period of dry weather in a dry summer, when irrigation requirements are high and the stream flow is low. If the flow is gauged in an average year there is every possibility of the source failing to provide enough water in dry years. Irrigation by direct abstraction is possible if the stream flow in a dry summer exceeds the irrigation requirement by a safe margin, after allowing for any downstream flow which the Water Authority may require, bearing in mind that in drought years the Authority can place further restrictions on the abstraction of water for spray irrigation.

About 80 per cent of the total annual stream flow occurs during the winter months, and because of this a stream which is found deficient in summer flow can sometimes provide enough water if winter flow can be stored in a reservoir and used as required in the summer months. To assess the winter flow with reasonable accuracy the stream should be gauged daily through the winter months and an estimate of the stream flow occurring in a dry winter can then by made by using the method described in Appendix G. Appendix F shows a typical series of winter stream flow gaugings and the calculations involved.

When, due to lack of time or some other reason, gauging is impracticable, resort must be made to an estimate of flow based on the gauging of some other stream for which records are available and allowing as far as possible for differences in catchment area, slopes, vegetation, rainfall and any other characteristics which may affect the flow. This method may also be used to provide a further estimate for comparison to that described in the above paragraph. Records of stream flow from small catchments, however, are scarce. Flow gauging for large catchments and whole river basins are available, covering long periods in some cases, but the runoff per hectare from an individual catchment or part of one, forming part of a larger catchment, may differ greatly from the runoff per hectare from the latter.

Two examples of flow records for large catchments with different characteristics are given below. These records and the notes above are intended only to give an insight into the problem and it is important to remember that small streams in the upper limit of catchments may dry up whilst quite susbstantial flows are being maintained downstream.

2

TABLE 1

Examples of winter runoff

River Stour, at Stratford St. Mary, Essex
Catchment area 85 500 hectares
Average annual rainfall 620 mm

Winter runoff for 25 consecutive years. 1935–59:

Winter runoff more than	12 mm	25 mm	50 mm	75 mm	100 mm	125 mm
Occurrence in years	25	24	21	13	8	4

Maximum runoff 152 mm   Minimum runoff 24 mm   Average runoff 86 mm

River Avon, at Warwick
Catchment area 220 000 hectares
Average annual rainfall 660 mm

Winter runoff for 22 consecutive years, 1938–59:

Winter runoff more than	25 mm	50 mm	75 mm	100 mm	125 mm	150 mm	175 mm	200 mm	225 mm
Occurence in years	22	21	18	16	13	99	7	4	1

Maximum runoff 240 mm   Minimum runoff 27 mm   Average runoff 138 mm

If the estimate indicates that the whole flow of the stream, even if available, would be insufficient, even with storage, the scheme will have to be reconsidered. If it appears that sufficient water may be available then the Water Authority should be consulted regarding a licence to abstract the amount required.

METHODS OF FLOW GAUGING

Flows in small watercourses can most conveniently be measured with the aid of a vee notch or rectangular weir. A vee notch weir is the best device for measuring small flows. A 150 mm vee notch is suitable for flows up to 12 litres per second and a 300 mm vee notch will measure flows up to 67 litres per second. For higher flows a rectangular weir is preferable. The notch or weir may be made of metal, timber or other material of adequate strength, but for accurate gauging the crest should be sharp; this can be achieved by using thin material or bevelling the edge of thick material on the downstream side. The weir or notch should be positioned in a straight and uniform length of channel, set at right angles to the direction of flow and extend well into the banks and stream bed for watertightness and stability, see Appendices D and E.

The height of the upstream water surface above the bottom of the vee notch or the crest of a rectangular weir determines the flow and if this height or head is measured by means of a graduated stake driven into the stream bed a metre or so upstream, the flow in litres per second or ha mm per day, corresponding to the measured head, can be found from either Appendix D or Appendix E, according to which type of flow gauge is being used. The appropriate Water Authority must be notified before any flow gauging apparatus is installed.

A very rough estimate of the flow in a small stream can be made by measuring the water cross-section where the channel is reasonably uniform and determining the mid-stream velocity by noting the time that a float takes to cover a known distance. The average stream velocity may be taken as 0·8 of the mid-stream or maximum velocity. The cross-sectional area in square metres multiplied by the average velocity in metres per second, and the answer multiplied by 1000, will give the stream flow in litres per second.

FIELD DRAINAGE

On many holdings the flow of water from the field underdrainage system may be a source worthy of consideration. Whether a system can provide sufficient water would depend upon the area covered by the system and the proportion of the rainfall which is accepted into the system. A gauge installed in a ditch just downstream of the main outfall, as described in Appendices D and E, will provide a good indication of how much water is available. As the flow from a system ceases before irrigation is needed, full winter storage is usually necessary. An abstraction licence may be required.

GROUND WATER

Subject to a licence being issued by the Water Authority, any type of well or borehole may be used to abstract water from below the water table, providing the yield is of satisfactory quality and sufficient in quantity to meet the irrigation demand.

OCCURRENCE

Rainfall, after meeting the need of plant transpiration, evaporation and surface runoff, will percolate into the soil and, if geological conditions allow, eventually reach the main storage of underground water in the water-bearing strata known as aquifers. The surface geology of an area determines the extent to which rainfall will run off as streams or percolate into the soil. The ability of aquifers to yield ground water into a well, either hand dug or bored, depends upon the physical nature of the aquifers such as the size of the pores and fissures and the degree of intercommunication between them. The principal water-bearing strata include sandstones, limestones and chalk. Drift deposits, such as river sands and gravel, can provide local supplies of ground water.

GROUND WATER ABSTRACTION

Geological advice on the prospects of obtaining ground water from a bore-hole or well, from the point of view of accessibility and chemical quality, can be obtained from the appropriate Water Authority or the Central Water Planning Unit, Resources Division, Reading Bridge House, Reading RG1 8PF. From an evaluation of the geological conditions and on the advice of a competent well sinker, the details of a scheme for abstracting ground water can be determined. The depth of a borehole will depend upon the depth and thickness of the water-bearing strata and may lie between 6 and 120 metres, although deeper boreholes are occasionally required. The diameter of boreholes for irrigation purposes will be between 150 mm and 450 mm, but the minimum diameter is usually governed by the size of pump required. Where water-bearing strata are fine-grained and unconsolidated, tending to 'run' when abstraction takes place, slotted lining tubes, sand screens or gravel packs are required. The length of lining tubes depends upon all these factors as well as the necessity to prevent ingress of surface pollution, or other waters of adverse chemical quality. Linings may be constructed of cast iron, mild steel, stainless steel, aluminium, plastic, concrete, asbestos, cement or brickwork, depending upon the circumstances. The use of wells is usually restricted to small systems but shallow sources of ground water can be utilized by means of a series of tube wells ('well points') sunk a short distance apart and connected to a common pump suction.

YIELD

Although the abstraction licence will state the quantity of the water authorized to be abstracted from the well or borehole during the period or periods specified, a properly conducted pumping test must be made to determine whether the well or borehole has sufficient potential to meet the demand. The test should extend over a sufficient length of time, at least 24 hours, to ensure that the demand rate can be maintained. The information obtained during the test will be useful in determining the final details of the permanent equipment to be installed.

PUBLIC SUPPLY

Information on the possibility of using public supply water for irrigation can be obtained from the local Water Undertaking, who can supply details of the quantity, pressure and cost of any supply which may be available and will advise whether supplies can be assured in dry periods. The capacity of rural water mains is usually insufficient for a direct supply to a farm without upsetting the functioning of the system elsewhere. Unless the requirements are very small, it will usually be necessary to provide storage equal to a day's requirement at peak demand so that water can be stored overnight, thus reducing the effect on mains pressure during the day. The cost of the water is likely to be too high for the lower value crops such as grass and sugar beet but may well be economic for high value crops such as early potatoes and market garden crops, for which the areas and water requirements tend to be much smaller.

Storage of Water

THE NEED FOR STORAGE

THE need for storage arises when the supply of water available is less than the flow of water required to meet the irrigation demand. The demand can be met if enough water is available at other times to make up the deficiency and sufficient storage is provided. Thus the need for storage and the amount of storage required can only be established after the amount of water available and the irrigation demand have been estimated in terms of inflow and outflow. This applies to water from all sources. The need to store public supply water will also depend upon the requirements of the Water Undertaking, but in most cases storage will be necessary.

TYPES OF RESERVOIRS

STORAGE OF SURFACE WATER

Surface water is the most usual source of irrigation water, and its conservation by way of farm storage will become increasingly important and necessary if irrigation is to develop. On most farms a certain amount of storage is possible, but the cost of storage will vary greatly depending on the topography and geology of the area.

Reservoirs for the storage of surface water can be grouped into two types, i.e., impounding and offstream. An impounding reservoir is usually referred to as one that is on the line of a watercourse and is created by means of a dam built across the valley. Arranged in this way it has to receive the whole of the flow from the catchment area and the overflow arrangements must be of sufficient size and strength to accept and pass storm flows past the dam when the reservoir is full. If the watercourse forms part of a farm boundary then the reservoir would encroach on neighbouring land. On a farm scale, impounding reservoirs with earth dams are only likely to be suitable where catchments are small and overflow works need not be too large or expensive. The offstream arrangement is usually possible and, generally, easier and cheaper.

Offstream reservoirs are constructed away from the main stream or, alternatively, the main stream is diverted to by-pass the reservoir which is then constructed on the site of the original channel. The essential characteristic of an offstream reservoir is that all the flow in the main stream can completely by-pass the reservoir when the latter is full; hence, the large and costly overflow arrangements needed for reservoirs of the impounding type are avoided. Offstream reservoirs offer much greater choice of site, e.g., they may be located where soil conditions are more suitable, or more centrally in the command area.

STORAGE OF FIELD DRAINAGE WATER

As the flow from a field underdrainage system ceases before irrigation is needed, full winter storage is necessary unless other water sources are

13

available during the irrigation season. The above comments on the storage of surface water apply equally to the storage of field drainage water.

Storage of Ground Water

The need for surface storage of ground water will not occur very often as, essentially, ground water is obtained from natural storage which exists in the aquifer. The problem is one of extracting the water at a sufficient rate to meet the demand.

If a single well or borehole cannot yield the water at the maximum rate required it has to be considered whether additional wells or boreholes would be a better solution than the provision of storage. Sometimes storage is proposed because the licensed abstraction rate is less than the rate at which the water is needed. This may be due to necessary restriction imposed by the Water Authority to avoid over-pumping the aquifer but it emphasizes the need to make sure the abstraction rate sought in the licence application is sufficient. The licenced maximum rates are usually based on the results of test pumping the aquifer.

Where storage is needed and the source is a superficial deposit of sand or gravel, then additional storage can be created simply by excavating over an area to a depth below the water table to form a seepage reservoir. The circumstances in which a seepage reservoir may be appropriate are discussed more fully on page 34.

Existing Storage

Ready made storage, drawing upon varying proportions of surface and ground water, may be available on some farms in the form of lakes, ponds, gravel, clay or other mineral workings. Some of these are of considerable size, but, although they may be standing full of water, which may have accumulated over a long period, the quantity of water which can be abstracted season after season may be less than their size suggests. This is especially so in the case of clay and marl pits, which are usually filled partly by rainfall and partly by the surface runoff from the surrounding ground. On the other hand some gravel pits have a considerable inflow of ground water and the same water may have been available by merely sinking a well, even if the gravel pit had not existed.

Small Reservoirs

For short-term storage, such as overnight storage of public supply water, sectional steel tanks circular in plan on a concrete base with butyl rubber linings are frequently used. Heavier gauge steel tanks, tanks made of reinforced plastics panels etc. or brick or concrete structures are also sometimes used. The design of such structures is not dealt with in this Bulletin as much information is available elsewhere and from the manufactures. For capacities of over 500 cubic metres an earth reservoir is likely to be the only economic solution and, if suitably lined, may also be an alternative at lesser capacities.

STORAGE CAPACITY

There is not necessarily any direct relationship between the irrigation demand and the amount of storage needed. The latter may be large or small to meet the same irrigation demand, depending upon how much water is available from the source and when it is available.

Nett Storage Capacity

The nett storage capacity must be sufficient to enable the maximum irrigation demand to be met whenever and however often it occurs. The nett volume must therefore be equal to the maximum difference between the cumulative available supply and the cumulative demand. At one extreme, the storage of a few hours inflow may be enough. At the other, it is necessary to store a whole season's requirement if water is available only outside the irrigation season, e.g., during the winter months.

Further information is provided in Appendix H.

Actual Storage Capacity

The actual storage capacity of a reservoir must be greater than the nett capacity to take into account the following factors:

1 *Evaporation losses*—The extent of these losses depends upon the weather conditions. They will form a higher proportion of the total water stored in a shallow reservoir than in a deep reservoir of the same capacity. This is because the shallow reservoir would have a greater surface area and the quantity of water lost through evaporation is proportional to the surface area. The losses may exceed 0·3 metres of water depth over the months of a dry summer.

2 *Seepage losses*—Seepage from unlined earth reservoirs varies with the permeability of the soil and the depth of water. It can be estimated from permeability tests of soil samples or on site testing. However, many sites contain varied soils and an extensive investigation is usually not a practical proposition for the type of storage reservoirs considered in this Bulletin. Estimates of the potential seepage losses made on the basis of limited tests must be assumed to have large margins of error. However, for soils generally suitable for unlined reservoir construction, a seepage loss of about 0·3 metres a year may be expected. Permeable soils such as sand and gravels would require waterproofing as described later.

3 *Dead water*—This is water which cannot be used because a reservoir should not and usually cannot be completely emptied whilst in service. The extent to which the water level can ultimately be drawn down will depend on the position of the outlet or pump suction pipe, but it is good practice to design on the basis of retaining at least 0·3 metres of water over as much of the floor of the reservoir as is reasonably practicable.

4 *Plant breakdown and firefighting*—In the case of short-term storage it may be of advantage to increase the capacity, for example from 24 hours storage to 3 days, to give some protection against failure in electricity or fuel supplies, breakdown of pumping equipment and also to prove a valuable source of water for firefighting.

Selection of Sites for Earth Reservoirs

THE choice of a site for a small earth reservoir on a farm may have to be reconciled with many factors other than engineering, such as proximity to the irrigated crops and layout of the farm. As soon as a site is selected trial holes should be sunk as described below to establish whether the soil is sufficiently impermeable to retain water adequately and whether there is enough suitable soil for embankment construction. If waterpoofing is needed then consideration should be given to the additional cost. If it is decided to proceed, a proper level survey leading to the preparation of a contoured site plan is the next step. Drawings for a reservoir of the required capacity can then be prepared, including details of any inlet and overflow works. It is then possible to assess the extent and amount of the earthworks involved, and hence to estimate the cost. Without this planning preparation the cost of a reservoir cannot be reasonably estimated, nor can a reservoir be constructed in any definite manner or for any definite purpose at any definite cost. It is assumed in the following paragraphs that the adequacy of a water source has been assessed as described on pages 6 to 12 and the required storage capacity determined as outlined on pages 14–15.

OFFSTREAM RESERVOIRS

SITE LOCATION

In many cases an offstream reservoir can be placed anywhere on the farm where suitable soil is available; thus land which has little or no agricultural value can sometimes be put to use. Occasionally levels permit the siting of the reservoir for gravity feed, which simplifies filling and avoids the complication and cost of pumping.

An adequate depth of impermeable soil over the site is essential unless some method of waterproofing is acceptable. Sites with clay or clay soils which extend well below the reservoir floor can be considered ideal. Sand, gravel, chalk and other porous soils will require lining. An underlying layer of impermeable soil can sometimes be used if enough of this material, of a suitable quality to construct the water retaining part of the embankments can be obtained by selecting suitable material excavated on site. Hence the importance of sufficient trial holes to estimate the extent of the various soil types. The cost of importing material with suitable clay content will depend upon the amount required and the length of haul, but may be prohibitive. Site accessibility is an important factor which is sometimes overlooked. The machine used in reservoir construction require an access road of adequate width and load carrying capacity and extra working space beyond the reservoir limits may be needed for staking material which has to be double-handled, e.g., topsoil. All vegetation should be removed from a reservoir site and as the cost of removing a dense covering of trees and shrubs is high, a site fairly free from vegetation is preferable.

WATER TO EARTH RATIO

Where a choice of site exists an important factor affecting the cost of construction is the water to earth ratio, i.e., the volume of water storage made available by the movement of a given volume of earth. For an entirely excavated reservoir with no storage above the orginal ground level, the ratio will be less than 1 : 1, allowing for freeboard and dead water. Unless some ready-made storage already exists, such as a clay pit, which would alter the water to earth ratio, the construction of an entirely excavated reservoir is uneconomical.

For a reservoir of a given capacity the water to earth ratio increases as the depth of water decreases to a practical minimum of about 2 metres. In most situations the depth of water is determined by the amount of land made available. Thus the maximum water to earth ratio is fixed by site conditions and is achieved by excavating only sufficient material from the reservoir floor area to construct the embankments. A reservoir so constructed has a final floor level below and a top embankment level above the original ground surface. The depth of excavation and the corresponding water to earth ratio, required for an offstream reservoir of a given storage capacity and depth of water, can be determined from Appendix K, Figs. 14, 15 and 16, and the method of use is fully described on page 20.

IMPOUNDING RESERVOIRS

SITE LOCATION

A dam can be built across a watercourse almost anywhere, but the construction of a satisfactory impounding reservoir requires a site on which the dam, the spillway and the reservoir can function as a satisfactory whole. As ideal sites are seldom available on a farm some compromise is usually necessary. If a compromise is made it should not involve any reduction in the capacity of the spillway or in the design standards for the dam, which are described later.

The amount and nature of material available for construction, the suitability of the dam foundation (see page 36), and the watertightness of the site are points to be considered. If the dam can be constructed of material excavated from within the reservoir site then the cost of importing material is avoided and the reservoir capacity is increased.

As the area occupied by an impounding reservoir is usually greater than that of an offstream reservoir of the same capacity, its shape being largely determined by the topography, waterproofing is likely to be uneconomic. Thus to avoid excessive seepage a site should be chosen where a layer of impermeable soil covers the floor area at or near the surface of the existing ground. If the floor area consists of permeable strata, such as gravel or sand, to a considerable depth, the site is unsuitable.

The dam must be sited on terrain which is stable and homogeneous. The watercourse downstream of the dam must be stable. Excessive bed slopes produce steps in the channel floor which may advance gradually upstream and undermine the dam. If there is any doubt, the channel should be stabilized by properly designed control weirs.

As in the case of offstream reservoirs the site should be accessible and free from excessive vegetation.

PROVISION FOR A SPILLWAY

The selection of a reservoir site which allows the construction of a spillway of adequate capacity and at a reasonable cost is of prime importance, and will depend upon the topography.

No hard and fast rules can be laid down. For example, in valleys having flat side slopes it is usually possible to construct a spillway in undisturbed ground in the side of the valley, around one end of the dam and discharging well clear of it. In valleys having steep side slopes the cost of the spillway may be so high in relation to the cost of the dam itself that the entire scheme may become uneconomic. Occasionally it is possible to construct a spillway through the valley side to discharge into a stream in an adjacent catchment. In all cases where the storm flow from one catchment is diverted into another, the danger of increasing the amount of storm flow in the adjacent water-course must be considered. If the catchment area of the adjacent watercourse is considerably smaller than the reservoired catchment area, then the effect of diverting storm flows into a watercourse of inadequate capacity may be disastrous. Spillway design is considered in detail on pages 30 to 33.

Although it is considered good practice to lead the spillway directly into a watercourse, in some cases it can be curtailed and the storm flow allowed to discharge over a wide area (see Fig. 23). The effect of this flow on the local topography must be considered. The approximate path that it will take should be located and, if excessive erosion is likely to occur or if there is the remotest chance of endangering the stability of the dam, then such a method should not be used.

WATER TO EARTH RATIO

The water to earth ratio for impounding reservoirs depends upon the longitudinal bed slope of the valley and the height of the dam, and is independent of the valley side slopes if these are uniform. Gently sloping valleys store more water for a particular height of dam than steep valleys. The effect of the valley bed slope and the dam height on the water to earth ratio can be seen in Appendix L, Fig. 18, which assumes evenly graded valleys, dams with a freeboard of 0·9 m, and that the dam material is excavated from within the area to be submerged. The water to earth ratio alone, however, does not determine the total cost; outlet, overflow and spillway works involve expenditure which is dependent upon other factors.

SITE INVESTIGATION

TRIAL HOLES

Trial holes are essential to find out whether a site is suitable for the construction of a reservoir and are usually sunk by power driven auger or mechanical digger. The soil samples obtained from the trial holes will provide information on the watertightness of the site and the suitability of the soil as a foundation for and for the construction of the embankment or dam. The trial holes should be sunk well below the full depth of any proposed excavation and should be plentiful in number over the reservoir floor and over any area which is to service as a foundation for the embankment or dam. The number and positioning of the holes is a matter of judgement, but as a minimum a trial hole should be sunk at each corner of the site and one in the middle. Further holes should then be sunk if necessary to confirm or investigate further the indications obtained from the initial trial holes. Particular attention must be paid to the permeability and consistency of the soil and to variations in the strata revealed. For example, a layer of clayey soil may overlie a gravel seam and, if the clay layer has to be removed or is naturally too thin, the site may be useless. The levels and inflow rate of any ground water encountered can indicate the degree of soil permeability and should be measured. Filling the holes with water and observing rates of loss will also give some indication, although the permeability of undisturbed soil may be different from soil that has been consolidated. If rock, sand or gravel is disclosed it will probably be impossible to construct a storage reservoir a a reasonable cost, and an alternative site should be sought. It is more usual to find an intermediate range of soils or mixtures of soil, many of which will be quite suitable for this type of dam or reservoir construction, provided they can contain sufficient clay material.

The cost of trial holes is well worthwhile. In reasonable soil, ten or more holes can easily be sunk in a working day with a light rubber-tyred excavator. These light machines can usually work down to a depth of 3 metres and some of them to a depth of 4 metres.

Existing Field Drains

The layout and location of existing field drains in or near the reservoir site should be established so that they can be intercepted, diverted and cut and plugged as necessary. Their presence, which may be entirely unsuspected, can increase the seepage losses from a reservoir to such a level that the effective capacity of the reservoir, which is otherwise soundly constructed, is severely reduced. Experience has shown that a surprisingly large zone of fissuring is often present in clay soils in the vicinity of established field drains. It is therefore a wise precaution to consolidate the soil in the vicinity of the original field drain.

Design of Earth Reservoirs

OFFSTREAM RESERVOIRS

OFFSTREAM reservoirs avoid some of the hazards of dam building and the need and expense of providing large capacity overflows. They may be formed wholly by excavation or by a combination of excavation and embanking. A wholly excavated reservoir requires more excavation for a given amount of storage than any other type but the saving in land and in some circumstances the advantage of gravity filling may outweight the higher excavation cost. Partly excavated and partly embanked reservoirs are usually the most economical. Typical layouts and main constructional features are illustrated in Appendix M.

RESERVOIR CAPACITY AND DIMENSIONS

Appendix K gives the dimensions required to construct a reservoir of any given capacity so that the soil excavated from the reservoir floor area will be of just sufficient amount to form the embankments, which should be constructed to the standards laid down on pages 36 to 47, and to such a height as to ensure a freeboard of 0·6 metres after settlement.

To use Appendix K the nett reservoir capacity required must first be determined by the methods outlined on pages 14 to 15. In the following example, it is assumed that such calculations have been performed and that a reservoir having a nett capacity of, say, 16 000 cubic metres is needed to store winter stream flow.

Following a farm survey a parcel of land is found to be available which is approximately rectangular in shape and of such a size as to allow the construction of an offstream reservoir having a perimeter of 370 metres. It should be remembered that the reservoir perimeter is measured along the centre-line of the embankment. Thus, as the nett reservoir capacity and perimeter are known, Fig. 14 can be used to determine the depth of water, which in this particular example is approximately 2·5 metres. However, in the case of winter storage, to compensate for seepage and evaporation, extra storage capacity is needed and, if detailed information is unavailable, as will probably be the case, a reasonable allowance to make is to increase the depth of water by 0·5 metres. The actual depth of water thus becomes 3·0 metres, which corresponds to an actual reservoir capacity of 18 000 cubic metres (see Fig. 14). The final embankment height is 3·0 plus 0·6 metres freeboard, i.e., 3·6 metres.

As the reservoir perimeter, actual capacity and depth of water are known, Fig. 15 can be used to determine the average depth of excavation over the reservoir floor area needed to produce sufficient soil for the construction of the embankment. On a sloping site the depth of excavation will vary and in this case the average depth of excavation is that which occurs in the centre of the floor area. Although Fig. 15 assumes that the reservoir is constructed on a level site, it can be used for gently sloping sites of a uniform nature, but the accuracy diminishes as the slope increases.

Thus, using a reservoir perimeter of 370 metres and a water depth of

3·0 metres in Fig. 15 produces an average depth of excavation of 1·25 metres and, using the same values in Fig. 16, gives a water to earth ratio of 2·6. As the volume of water is 18 000 cubic metres about 7000 cubic metres of consolidated soil is required for the construction of the embankment.

This example assumes that full use is made of the land available and in most cases this will give the lowest capital cost of construction for a reservoir of given nett capacity. As a general rule the capital cost decreases as the actual depth of water decreases to a practical minimum of 2 metres. For water depths below 2 metres the cost per cubic metre of nett capacity tends to rise. Large shallow reservoirs may appear economic on paper in terms of the amount of earth moving required but potential problems are excessive weed growth, high evaporation losses, a large proportion of dead water and a surplus of topsoil.

GRAVITY SUPPLY

An offstream reservoir can be filled or partly filled by gravity from an adjacent stream in so far as it can be arranged so that the water level in the reservoir is below the water level in the stream at the intake, by an amount which will provide a reasonable fall in the feeder channel or pipe. Gravity-fed reservoirs are usually constructed on or near the plain of the watercourse, a practice which is not recommended where there is a risk of flooding.

FEEDER CHANNEL OR PIPE

The flow to a gravity-fed reservoir may be conveyed by a channel or by a pipeline, see Appendix M, Fig. 19. Feeder channels should be of adequate size and constructed at such a slope as to ensure that the velocity at maximum flow will not cause erosion. Maximum channel velocities and slopes for various types of soils are given in the following table.

TABLE 2

Maximum channel velocities and slopes

Soil type	Maximum velocity	Maximum slope
sandy soil	0·6 m/sec	1 in 600
loam	0·9 m/sec	1 in 300
clay	1·2 m/sec	1 in 150

If the reservoir and intake levels are such that the velocity in a feeder channel would exceed the maximum for a particular soil type then a feeder pipe should be used.

The channel should terminate with a headwall before reaching the reservoir and the flow should be taken through the embankment in a pipe of sufficient size to pass the maximum inflow. To prevent bank erosion whenever the level of the water in the reservoir is below the inlet pipe, the end of the pipe should discharge on to an apron of hard material extending down to the reservoir bottom, or the pipe itself can be extended downwards ending at a small apron, see Appendix M, Fig. 21. Alternatively, the pipe can be taken out into the reservoir and, if it discharges well clear of the embankment, then the hard aprons can be omitted. In this case the pipe will have to be supported off the reservoir floor. Similar precautions are necessary in a lined reservoir to prevent damage to the lining.

PUMPED SUPPLY

Filling by pumping gives a much wider scope for finding a good site. Pump-fed reservoirs can usually be located anywhere on the farm and, in particular, on land which has little agricultural value. Offsetting these advantages is the cost of pumping for long periods. A typical layout is shown in Appendix M, Fig. 20.

PUMPING COSTS

Capital costs of pumping equipment are considered in Appendix C. Running costs can vary widely, but if no other information is available then a figure of £10 per annum per irrigated hectare is an indication of the running costs for the reservoir filling pump. To keep pumping costs to a minimum, the whole pumping system, and particularly the pump unit, should be carefully designed to operate at maximum efficiency. If electric power is available an automatic pumping unit offers much advantage unless it is possible and preferable to abstract at a very high rate for short periods, when a manually controlled unit powered by an internal combustion engine would be suitable.

PUMP SELECTION

The maximum rate at which water can be pumped from a stream, limited either by the amount of water available or by restrictions imposed by the abstraction licence, together with the total head required, will determine the pump duty. A practical basis for winter storage is to assume that the reservoir can be filled in 1000 hours pumping time. For a reservoir of 18 000 cubic metres capacity this would mean a pump capable of delivering 18 cubic metres per hour or 5 litres per second.

The pump selected must be capable of lifting the required amount of water against a head at least equal to the sum of the following:

    (a) the vertical lift, measured in metres, from the minimum water level at the pump intake to the highest point reached by the delivery pipe

and

    (b) an amount, expressed in metres head, to offset the friction losses in the suction and delivery pipes

and

    (c) an amount, expressed in metres head, to offset the losses due to pipe fittings, particularly valves, elbows and T-junctions. Assumed to be 25 per cent of (b) for short pipe runs.

Such factors as the size, length and condition of the suction and delivery pipes and the rate at which the water is to be pumped will influence the value of (b) and therefore (c). Table 3 gives the friction losses in metres

TABLE 3

Friction losses in smooth pipes in good condition

Friction losses in metres per 100 metres of pipe

Pipe dia: mm	Pipe flow in litres per second																
	1	2	3	4	5	6	7	8	9	10	12	14	16	18	20	25	30
50		2·2															
75	0·1	0·3	0·7	1·1	1·7	2·4											
100				0·3	0·4	0·6	0·8	0·9	1·2	1·4	2·0						
125								0·3	0·4	0·5	0·7	1·0	1·2	1·6	1·8		
150											0·3	0·4	0·5	0·6	0·8	1·1	1·4
175														0·3	0·3	0·5	0·7
200																0·3	0·3

head per 100 metres of smooth pipe in good condition with well-aligned joints.

Taking the above example, if the length of the pipe run is 100 metres and the diameter is 100 mm, the friction loss from Table 3 would be less than 1 metre. If the total vertical lift is, say, 7 metres then a pump capable of delivering 5 litres per second against a total head of, say, 10 metres would be a satisfactory arrangement.

Pump and Delivery Pipe

The pump should be sited as near the stream as possible and in such a position that the pump suction does not exceed 5 metres in height. The pump output falls as the suction lift increases.

Unless the stream has sufficient depth, it will be necessary to construct a pumping sump, either by means of a weir built across the stream to increase the depth of water or by digging out the bed of the stream. If the stream flow is liable to fluctuate below the pumping rate, or the abstraction rate is limited, the sump will have to provide sufficient storage to prevent excessive stopping and starting of the pump. The pump suction must be kept clear of the sump bottom and some form of screening against weeds and floating debris will be necessary. Water discharging from the delivery pipe into the reservoir close to the side must fall on to an apron of hard material to prevent damage to the embankment. Alternatively, as in the case of gravity supply, the pipe can be carried down near the floor to discharge on to a small apron, but a small hole should be drilled at the summit of the pipe to prevent any possibility of the water siphoning back out of the reservoir when the pump is stopped. Another method is to carry the pipe well out into the reservoir beyond the embankment, ensuring that the pipe is adequately supported and restrained against excessive movement.

Overflow Arrangements

The overflow from a gravity-fed offstream reservoir is best constructed, if site conditions permit, in the bank of the feeder channel so that surplus water is diverted back to the stream before reaching the reservoir. Also the amount of silt entering the reservoir can be controlled. Some silt in suspension can be beneficial in reducing seepage losses in a new reservoir. If the fall of the feeder channel and the stream is such that the construction of an overflow channel is impossible, or if a feeder pipe is used, then recourse must be made to an overflow pipe built through the embankment or preferably in undisturbed ground if the design of the reservoir permits discharging at some point downstream of the intake. The capacity of the overflow pipe should be greater than the capacity of the inlet channel or pipe.

The best arrangement of the overflow from a pump-fed reservoir is an overflow pipe, as described above, discharging into any convenient watercourse which can accept the maximum flow. The capacity of the overflow should be equal to the maximum inflow rate, i.e., the pump output.

All pipe overflows should be designed and constructed, for the approximate capacity, as described on page 27 for separate primary overflows in impounding reservoirs. Taking a typical example, if the required overflow capacity is 100 litres per second or 0·1 cumecs, then the first line of Table 4 on page 28 gives the length of the overflow weir as 0·3 metres; this is in fact a practical minimum size for pipe overflows regardless of capacity. The diameter of the overflow pipe is determined by its slope as indicated in Table 4 and Fig. 1. For the smaller flows an overflow pipe with an upturned bend and bellmouth inlet of sufficient lip length will suffice. A trash ring or other protection against blockage is desirable.

STREAM CONTROL WEIRS

Where the abstraction rate from a stream is restricted, the inflow to the reservoir or pumping sump can be controlled by a weir across the feeder channel or across the entrance to the intake pipe. In small watercourses a weir may also be needed across the main stream to raise the water level sufficiently for the entrance weir to be effective. The relative levels and widths of the two weirs, in the latter case, will determine the proportion of the flow in each of the channels. The height of the weir in the main stream should be kept to a minimum. A low weir is more easily constructed, is less costly and has less effect on the upstream water levels. Removable weir boards are an advantage since they can be used to adjust water levels or can be removed to leave an unobstructed channel. A hole in the weir wall below the crest level is a useful method for maintaining a reasonably constant downstream flow, because the flow through the hole is not sensitive to changes in water level. Before stream control weirs or similar arrangements are constructed an impounding licence must be obtained from the Water Authority.

IMPOUNDING RESERVOIRS

An impounding reservoir, formed by constructing a dam across a stream, receives the whole of the flow from the stream catchment area. An overflow must be provided to convey surplus water past the dam when the reservoir is full; an outlet at a low level may be required under the terms of an impounding licence to enable a residual flow to be maintained downstream when the reservoir is not overflowing. The layout and main constructional features are illustrated in Appendix N.

THE DAM

For the amount of storage usually needed for irrigation, earth is the only economical material for the construction of the dam. The use of concrete, for example, will be altogether too costly unless the storage is for hundreds rather than thousands of cubic metres. Earth dams are basically no different from embankments required for offstream reservoirs of comparable height above the surrounding ground, and are discussed on pages 36 to 47.

RESERVOIR CAPACITY AND DIMENSIONS

Impounding reservoirs can achieve a high ratio of water stored to earth moved for a favourable site but the ratio reduces with the height of the dam which, for farm storage, is comparatively small.

Figures 17 and 18, Appendix L, give the required maximum height of dam and the corresponding water to earth ratio for a given reservoir capacity and valley shape. Although the conditions assumed in the diagrams are ideal and rarely encountered in practice, they can be used in the initial design stage to assess the potentiality of a particular site.

The methods using Figs. 17 and 18 may be best illustrated by taking a nett reservoir capacity of, say, 16 000 cubic metres and using this capacity to determine the maximum depth of water, the actual reservoir capacity and the volume of the dam of an impounding reservoir constructed in a valley having, for example, a bed slope of 1 in 50 and side slopes of 1 in 20.

Using the above data in Fig. 17, it is found that the required maximum depth of water at the dam is 3·2 metres. However, in the case of winter storage, to compensate for seepage and evaporation extra storage capacity is needed and, if detailed information is unavailable (as will probably be the case) a reasonable allowance to make is to increase the depth of water by 0·5 metres. The actual maximum depth of water thus becomes 3·7 metres, which corresponds to an actual reservoir capacity of 25 000 cubic metres.

As the actual reservoir capacity and maximum depth of water are known, Fig. 18 is used to determine the water to earth ratio and the volume of the dam, which in this particular example is 6·6 and about 4000 cubic metres respectively. Thus the amount of soil required to be moved is about 50 per cent of that for the equivalent offstream reservoir. The overall length of the reservoir, which may in some cases preclude the use of a site, can be found by multiplying the actual maximum depth of water at the dam by the valley bed slope, i.e., 3·7×50=185 metres. The maximum final height of the dam is 3·7 metres +0·9 metres freeboard, i.e., 4·6 metres.

Overflows

The overflow arrangements must be of sufficient capacity, strength and durability to deal with the maximum storm flow when the reservoir is full since, by definition, an impounding reservoir must receive the whole flow that arrives from the catchment. If the capacity of the overflow weir and channel is insufficient the dam may be washed away, which, apart from the destruction of the reservoir, may cause flooding, damage and possibly loss of life downstream. The dangers of inadequate overflows cannot be over-emphasized, particularly as the variation between normal and peak flows can be very great indeed.

The overflow arrangements described below assume that if the dam collapsed because of overtopping there would be no risk of significant damage to property or loss of life. If there is a risk, however remote, then the suggested size of the spillway should be increased and it is strongly recommended that advice should be sought from a chartered civil engineer experienced in these matters.

The dimensions and cost of the overflow works tend to become disproportionate and uneconomic for other than small catchments. In steeply sloping catchments with thin soils and vegetation, farm type impounding storage is often unsuitable for catchment areas greater than 100 hectares because of the width of the spillway channel which would be needed. For flat lowland catchments this limit may be doubled or even more but, wherever possible, it is preferable to construct an offstream reservoir, the inflow to which can be limited and the need for large overflow works avoided.

Overflow Arrangement and Design

The overflow arrangements have to be specially designed for a particular catchment area and reservoir site. In some cases ample provision can be made quite simply and cheaply, in others it may be difficult and costly, possibly uneconomic. The basic requirements are that the overflows must be of adequate capacity to pass the design storm flow with sufficient freeboard against overtopping of the dam and must be able to withstand erosion for such periods as the flows are likely to occur.

A single overflow, if used, must have adequate capacity to pass all flows up to the design storm flow and, as it would be in continuous use, must be constructed of material with a high resistance to long-term erosion. This type of overflow is usually only suitable for very small catchment areas; separate overflows for low and high flows are likely to be more economic in most cases.

The following notes assume that low flows are accepted by the *primary overflow* constructed of material, such as concrete, with a high resistance to long-term erosion, and for higher flows a separate *storm overflow* or *spillway* will come into operation. The latter will be used only rarely and is normally an earth channel protected by a dense cover of grass.

Primary Overflow Capacity

To ensure that the storm overflow or spillway only comes into operation at infrequent intervals, the primary overflow should be based on storm flows which are likely to occur in most years; a reasonable basis for design is 25 per cent of the *design storm flow* as given in Fig. 2 for a particular catchment size and slope. Table 4 gives the length of overflow weir and overflow pipe diameters for a given capacity, based on a weir capacity of 0·3 cumecs per metre length of weir at 0·3 metre head over the weir. To maintain the design flow in the overflow pipe the outfall arrangement should be such as to ensure that the outlet to the pipe is submerged. See Fig. 26.

Primary Overflow Arrangement

For small catchments the simplest form of primary overflow consists of a brick or concrete weir chamber sited in undisturbed ground at the edge of the reservoir, clear of the end of the dam and opposite to the spillway. The flow into the weir chamber is taken away by a pipe, with watertight joints, laid at an even slope in undisturbed ground to the watercourse downstream of the dam. The top of the chamber functions as a weir and controls the maximum level and capacity of the reservoir when it is not overflowing. To avoid undue loss of storage capacity, the primary weir level is set only sufficiently below the spillway crest (see Fig. 1 and Appendix N) to ensure that the primary overflow can take place without any flow passing through the spillway. A reasonable level is 0·3 metres below the spillway crest, so that there will be a freeboard of 0·9 metres when the reservoir is full but not overflowing, assuming that the spillway crest is set 0·6 metres below the dam crest. The length of the weir (i.e., the top of the chamber), the pipe diameter and fall must be sufficient to pass the design discharge. Also the entrance to the pipe must be set at least 1 metre below the weir to enable the necessary velocity to be developed to maintain the flow in the pipe. As the

TABLE 4

Primary overflow sizes

The primary overflow should be designed to pass at least 25 per cent of the design storm flow obtained from Fig. 2.

Capacity of overflow (cumecs)	Minimum length of inlet weir (m)	Length of pipe needed ÷ head available L/H (see Fig. 1)	Minimum diameter of overflow pipe (mm)
0·1	0·3	5 10 20 40	175 200 225 250
0·2	0·6	5 10 20 40	200 250 275 325
0·3	1	5 10 20 40	250 300 325 375
0·6	2	5 10 20 40	325 375 425 475
0·9	3	5 10 20 40	375 450 500 550
1·2	4	5 10 20 40	425 500 550 625
1·5	5	5 10 20 40	450 525 600 675
1·8	6	5 10 20 40	475 575 650 725

chamber is close to the valley side, the latter should be protected against erosion by extending the back wall of the chamber upwards and suitable screening should be provided to prevent the entry of floating debris, see Appendix N, Fig. 25.

An alternative arrangement of the primary overflow is a vertical pipe, the upper end of which functions as a circular weir and the lower end of which is connected into a pipeline passing at a slight fall below the dam, see

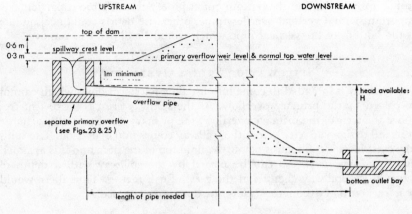

SEPARATE PRIMARY OVERFLOW

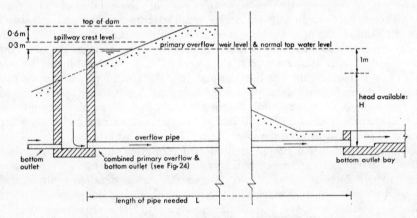

COMBINED PRIMARY OVERFLOW AND BOTTOM OUTLET

Fig. 1. Primary overflow arrangement

Note: The drawings are diagrammatic and for construction details see Appendix N. The size of overflow pipe for a particular size of overflow depends upon the ratio of L to H, see Table 4.

Appendix N, Fig. 24. This pipeline serves also as an outlet from the lowest level of the reservoir to maintain the flow in the watercourse downstream of the dam as is usually required by the impounding licence. It is also useful during the construction period for the same reason. Access to the top of the overflow pipe for valve operation can be provided by means of a light footbridge and the diameter of the pipe should be sufficient to permit access by means of a ladder or step irons for maintenance purposes. This type of overflow may be more difficult and expensive to construct than the chamber inlet type previously described. It also has the disadvantage of requiring a large diameter pipe under the dam instead of a much smaller pipe which would be needed solely as a bottom outlet. Its only advantage is to enable the vertical overflow pipe to be used as a valve shaft when a valve is placed on the upstream end of the bottom outlet pipe. Screening too is particularly important with a vertical overflow pipe, otherwise debris could accumulate at the bottom of the vertical pipe which would be difficult to remove.

Spillway or Storm Overflow

The spillway is intended to come into use only for storm flows which cannot be passed by the primary overflow. As the spillway crest is set 0·3 metres above the weir of the primary overflow, the primary overflow will discharge at its full design capacity before the spillway comes into operation. The spillway crest level is 0·6 metres below the final top of the dam and it is assumed that the *design storm flow* can be passed by the spillway with a depth of water in the spillway channel at the crest of 0·4 metres. Thus there would be a freeboard of 0·2 metres before the dam is overtopped.

Design Storm Flow

There is no simple method of accurately assessing the amount of storm flow which can occur from any particular small catchment. The characteristics of the rainfall, the area and shape of the catchment, its permeability, slopes and vegetation all affect the rate at which water may arrive at the reservoir site. The smaller the catchment, the steeper the slope, the thinner the soil and vegetation and the less the permeability, the greater will be the magnitude of storm flow per hectare of the catchment. Steep rocky upland catchments in high average rainfall regions are likely to produce high storm flows per hectare; on the other hand flat permeable catchments in low average rainfall regions will produce lower storm flows per hectare.

Figure 2 provides a simple method of determining the design storm flow from a particular catchment and should be used for catchments up to 200 hectares (subject to what is said on page 26) when detailed hydrological information is not available. The method of obtaining information on the average catchment slope, the catchment area and the average annual rainfall is described in Appendix A.

Size of Spillway Channel

The design storm flow obtained from Fig. 2 is used in Fig. 3 to obtain the bottom width of the spillway channel at the spillway crest. Although the primary overflow will be taking 25 per cent of the design storm flow when the spillway comes into operation this fact is disregarded in the determination of the spillway size, to provide a safety margin.

Spillway Arrangement

Although the usual spillway location is that illustrated in Appendix N, there are other alternatives, some of which are outlined on page 18. To ensure that the spillway will pass the design storm flow it is essential that, wherever the spillway is situated, the recommendations outlined below and in Appendix N are put into practice.

The capacity of the spillway depends upon the control section, which is a level straight portion of channel extending a distance of about 8 metres downstream from the spillway crest. The function of the control section is

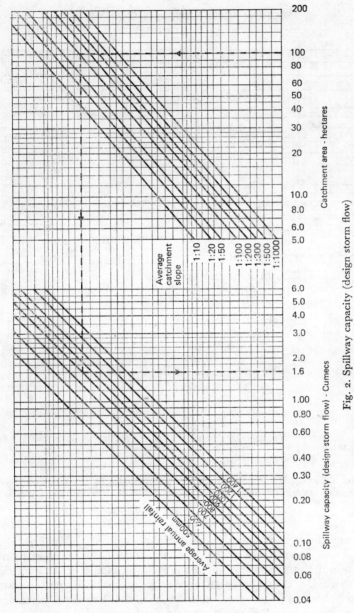

Catchment area - hectares

Spillway capacity (design storm flow)

Average catchment slope

1:10
1:20
1:50
1:100
1:200
1:300
1:500
1:1000

Spillway capacity (design storm flow) - Cumecs

Average annual rainfall

Fig. 2. Spillway capacity (design storm flow)

Example: A reservoir impounds a catchment of 100 hectares with an average slope of 1 in 100. The average annual rainfall is 800 mm. From the diagram the required spillway capacity is 1·6 cumecs. But see page 26.

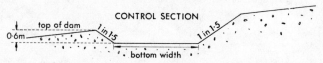

SECTION ACROSS SPILLWAY CHANNEL
(see Fig.23 for further details)

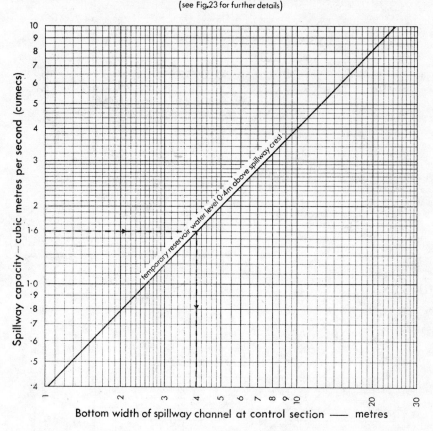

Fig. 3. Size of spillway channel

Example: From the example in Fig. 2 the required spillway capacity is 1·6 cumecs. Using this value in the above diagram gives the bottom width of the spillway as 4 metres.

to convert any rise in the reservoir water level above the spillway crest into a controlled flow downstream of the dam. To guide the water towards the control section the upstream portion of the spillway should act as a funnel, and thus the width of the spillway entrance at the normal reservoir top water level should be about 1½ times the bottom width of the channel at the control section. The upstream funnel portion should rise towards the control section at a slope of at least 1 in 40 and be such that the spillway entrance is below the normal reservoir top water level by about 0·2 metres. This makes certain that the funnel action comes into operation at any significant rise in reservoir water level. The downstream portion of the spillway channel should fall at a slope of 1 in 40 to maintain a channel velocity of approximately 1·5 metres per second, which is the maximum allowable if the erosion of the grassed spillway surface is to be kept within reasonable limits.

Protection of Spillway Against Erosion

A maximum spillway channel velocity of 1·5 metres per second assumes a dense cover of well-established grass. Hence the laying of turfs or sowing of seed should follow as soon as possible on the final trimming of the excavation. Turfing is the safest and quickest method but if the overflow is likely to come into use before the turfs have properly knitted to the underlying soil, they should be staked or wired. The use of reinforced bituminous, or butyl rubber, sheeting may be economical where better erosion protection is called for. Some notes on these materials are given on pages 48 and 49. If grass is used it should be a low maintenance species, because access is normally restricted. Perennial ryegrass should be avoided and less vigorous species such as creeping red fescue, chewing fescue, smooth stalked meadow grass and Browntop should be used. These grasses are not only slow growing, but also provide a dense cover and the root formation binds the topsoil.

Bottom Outlet Pipe

An outlet pipe from the bottom of the reservoir is needed in all cases where a residual flow must be maintained downstream, in accordance with the terms of the impounding licence. If the holding is a large one and the irrigated area, or part of it, lies far downstream of the reservoir, a bottom outlet may save the capital outlay on a main pipeline by enabling the stream itself to carry the water to a convenient point of abstraction. It also enables the reservoir to be emptied easily so that it can be cleaned out and repairs made. A combined primary overflow and bottom outlet pipe has alreay been described above. With this arrangement the bottom outlet pipe must be of larger diameter in order to cope with the primary overflow. Where a separate primary overflow and bottom outlet is provided, the bottom outlet pipe can usually be of small diameter but should not be less than 150 mm.

A pipe laid below the dam must be able to withstand any settlement of the embankment. It can also provide a possible seepage path along the outside of the pipe which may result in erosion and endanger the dam. Also at its upstream end the pipe has to withstand the water pressure produced by the full depth of water in the reservoir and any leakage from the pipe will also cause dangerous erosion. Hence the pipeline needs to be of sufficient strength and flexibility, watertight and should be carefully laid in a trench excavated in undisturbed ground. The control valve should preferably be at the upstream end, so that the pipe is not under pressure when the valve is closed but, as described above, this would mean an access bridge to a structure above the valve. Reservoir pipe work is described in detail on pages 45 to 47.

The entrance to the bottom outlet should be located well clear of the upstream toe of the dam and should be 150 mm or so above the bottom of the reservoir, to allow for silting. The location of the end of the pipe in a deep pocket should be avoided in favour of an open level area. A trash screen over the end of the pipe is necessary to prevent submerged debris entering the pipe and the floor of the inlet chamber should be at least 150 mm below the invert of the pipe.

BOTTOM OUTLET BAY

The downstream end of the outlet pipe should be carried well beyond the toe of the dam and allowed to discharge into the watercourse. If the outlet pipe velocity is high, as it is likely to be when the reservoir is full or over-flowing, then some means of protecting the watercourse from excessive erosion is required. In Appendix N, Fig. 26, a structure is shown which will reduce the high pipe velocity to an acceptable amount. This structure can be used wherever water moving at high velocity enters a watercourse, e.g., the outlet from a separate primary overflow.

SEEPAGE RESERVOIRS

In many areas permeable surface deposits, such as gravel, resting on impermeable beds, such as clay, can sometimes provide sufficient water for irrigation if shallow excavations are made exposing the water table and thus forming a seepage reservoir. This is only possible where the water table is close to the surface of the ground.

WATER AVAILABLE

The water available in permeable surface deposits is derived directly from percolating rainfall or in some instances from adjacent watercourses. In the former case the amount of water available depends upon the surface area covered by the permeable deposit. For example, if 150 mm of rainfall is estimated to percolate in a dry year and the maximum seasonal irrigation demand is 150 mm over 10 hectares, then the permeable catchment area must be at least 10 hectares. The permeable deposit is itself a reservoir and the problem is to abstract the necessary water at a sufficient rate. This may be done by either a system of wells or a much larger excavation, i.e., a seepage reservoir.

NEED FOR SEEPAGE RESERVOIRS

If the yield from such a system of wells is insufficient to meet the demand because of the slow rate of inflow, the construction of a seepage reservoir may be cheaper than sinking additional wells. In the construction of a seepage reservoir the material excavated from below the water table is replaced by water and the extra storage gained is equal to the volume of the material removed from below the water table. The effect of a large excavation in these circumstances is twofold. First, the rate of inflow into the reservoir is increased compared to a well because of the larger area of permeable surface exposed. The second effect is the creation of storage so that the slow inflow can be accumulated over a longer period to meet a higher rate of demand during a shorter period. In the latter respect the storage function is no different from that which is fulfilled in the case of other kinds of storage reservoirs. The water table exposed in a seepage reservoir is the water surface of the underground reservoir, and is continuous with it. Consequently, the rest level of the exposed surface will fluctuate with the level of the ground water table and the bottom of the excavation must be sufficiently below the lowest level of the water table to ensure adequate inflow and reservoir capacity.

Yield Testing

In most cases a yield test by pumping is necessary to find out whether the total amount of underground water available, exposed and hidden, is adequate to meet the total seasonal demand and whether the inflow rate is sufficient to meet the demand at any particular time. The rate of test pumping should be at least equal to that which will be required in practice. The duration of the test depends upon the results as they become available.

The water level and time at the beginning and end of each test and at regular intervals should be recorded, also the rate at which the water level recovers after pumping is stopped. If the water level falls measurably after each session and does not recover, this indicates that the total water reserves are not unlimited compared with the demand. The drop in rest level may be compared to the drop in level when pumping from a watertight reservoir and is a direct indication of the volume of water present. If the water level drops quickly but quickly recovers to the original level when pumping ceases, then it has to be considered whether increasing the area or depth of the excavation is likely to increase the rate of inflow sufficiently for the purpose of the scheme.

The time of year and the past weather pattern are significant factors which should be considered in conjuction with the results of a yield test. A series of dry winters and summers can reduce the water table and the corresponding rest water level to such an extent that a reservoir tested satisfactorily in a wet period may dry out. The reduced rest level can be re-exposed if the reservoir is deepened, assuming that a sufficient depth of permeable deposits is available. Some permeable deposits, such as sands, may be too unstable to be used for a seepage reservoir and other methods of abstracting the water, such as well points, should be considered.

A suitable report form for recording yield test data is shown in Appendix O. The recording of the data is vital to the usefulness of the test.

Design and Construction of Earth Embankments and Dams

GENERAL PRINCIPLES

THE two principal requirements for the safe construction of a water-retaining earth embankment or dam are that it must be structually stable under all conditions and sufficiently watertight. Although 'embankment' and 'dam' are normally used to describe the water-retaining earth structure of an offstream reservoir and impounding reservoir respectively, from the point of view of design and construction they are synonymous and for the purpose of this section 'embankment' will be used to cover both cases.

The stability of low embankments depends upon the type of soil used in the construction of the embankment, the type of soil underlying the embankment, the slope of the upstream and downstream faces, the overall width, and the measures taken to prevent surface and internal erosion. The stability also depends greatly upon the care with which an embankment is constructed and the extent to which the design provisions are put into effect. The stability of excavated slopes also needs careful consideration.

The resistance of the foundation soil and of the embankment itself to the flow of water is important, not only because of the water lost, but also because seepage may cause internal erosion and subsequent collapse of the embankment. This may happen even though the amount of water lost may not otherwise be significant. Erosion proceeds slowly at first, the minute streams of water carrying away the finer particles of the soil, but at a certain stage the rate of erosion increases rapidly and is followed by the sudden collapse of a section of the embankment. This process of internal erosion is sometimes referrred to as 'piping'.

It is not possible to construct an earth embankment which is completely watertight. Seepage, however insignificant, will always occur. Thus, to ensure stability, the embankment and foundation should be designed so that the rate of seepage is reduced to a minimum and seepage paths are adequately controlled.

To some extent foundations and embankments are considered separately in the following paragraphs but it should be borne in mind that, to be an effective and durable water-retaining structure, the embankment and its foundation must be designed and constructed as one unit.

FOUNDATIONS

STABILITY

A satisfactory foundation for a dam must be strong enough to support the weight of the embankment without undue settlement or displacement and must provide adequate resistance to sliding. Most soils have sufficient strength to bear the weight of the low embankments being considered here but peat, topsoil or any soil containing organic matter is unsuitable and must be stripped off and removed from the site. The sliding of the embankment on its foundation due to the horizontal thrust of the water is unlikely to occur unless the site slopes are very steep. In all cases the embankment site should be level or sloping towards the reservoir for additional safety.

Seepage Control

The question of soil impermeability is dealt with in detail in the paragraph on suitable soils for embankments on page 38. The soil proportions described also apply to foundations. Seepage through permeable foundation soils which overlie an impermeable layer can be controlled by constructing a cut-off wall along the line of the embankment, see Fig. 5 and 6. A trench of sufficient width is excavated down to the impermeable layer and is filled with soil which has a suitable clay content. The method of filling the cut-off wall with soil is the same as that described below for the construction of the embankment. Bentonite (see page 50) mixed with a permeable soil, such as some sands and gravels, produces an impermeable material which is suitable for cut-off filling.

An earth embankment founded on rock will be a relatively costly structure because of the need to excavate a cut-off trench in the rock to control seepage along the fissures in the rock surface. In the older rocks only a shallow trench may be needed to get below the surface fissures into compact rock but stratified rock will require greater depths owing to the existence of many deep-seated water-bearing fissures and may be a very costly operation. In most circumstances it is unlikely that an embankment can be constructed on rock within the economic limits of farm irrigation.

In all cases where a cut-off wall is necessary it must completely bridge the gap between the impermeable layer below and the embankment above.

Site Preparation

Trees, scrub, roots and all vegetation should be removed from the entire reservoir site. All topsoil should be stripped from the embankment site and put to one side for re-use in soiling the slopes and the top of the embankment. The embankment site should be levelled and the exposed subsoil ploughed, scarified or disced in a direction along the line of the embankment. This will improve the seal between the embankment and the foundation by creating parallel corrugations at right angles to the line of possible seepage flow. The sides of all pits, holes and the cut-off trench, if used, should be sloped at about $1\frac{1}{2}$: 1 to provide a satisfactory bond with the fill.

Bottom Outlet Pipe

Bottom outlet pipes are usually required for impounding reservoirs, for reasons explained on page 33. As the pipe is laid underneath the embankment it must be adequately protected against failure as the embankment settles, i.e., it must be flexible and must be so designed that water cannot pass underneath the embankment, with all the inherent risks, by seeping along the outside of the pipe. The best method of laying the pipe is in a trench excavated in the undisturbed foundation soil to a depth equal to 2 pipe diameters. Anti-seepage collars should be provided as described on page 47 and should pass through the walls of the excavated trench into undisturbed soil. The pipe trench should be refilled with soil, with a high clay content, which must be thoroughly compacted around the pipe and collars. Filling and compacting the soil around the lower half of the pipe is difficult and should be given special attention. Incomplete filling and compaction will lead to severe leakage problems which are difficult and costly to correct after the embankment is built. This also applies to pump suction pipework which is laid through an embankment, usually to avoid high suction lifts.

EMBANKMENTS

SUITABLE SOILS

The ideal soil to use for the satisfactory homogeneous construction of an earth embankment (see below) contains not less than 20 per cent, nor more than 30 per cent of clay, the remainder being *well graded* sand and gravel. Such a soil is stable even when subject to significant changes in moisture content. On the other hand a soil with a high clay content expands when wet and contracts and cracks on drying out and should preferably only be used in zoned construction (see below). If it is used for homogeneous construction, surface cracking and erosion will occur and adequate maintenance is essential.

SOIL TESTING

The proportions of the various component materials that form a particular soil may be estimated with reasonable accuracy by making the following test. Half fill a narrow parallel-sided glass bottle with a representative sample of the soil. Fill the bottle with water and shake well to mix the soil and water thoroughly. If waterglass (sodium silicate) is available add 2 or 3 drops to the water and stir the soil and water mixture vigorously. Stand the bottle on a firm surface and allow the soil to settle for 24 hours. Coarse sand will settle out immediately, fine sand within a few minutes and the silt and clay last. These will stratify into clearly visible layers from which the approximate solid proportions can be estimated by measuring the depth of each layer with a foot rule. Fig. 4 illustrates the soil test and the method of assessing the soil proportions.

Alternatively the soil samples can be sent for laboratory examination. The cost should be small compared to the cost of the reservoir and may be worthwhile where there is some doubt on the water-retaining characteristics of the soil.

TYPES OF CONSTRUCTION

Embankments may be placed into three categories according to the method of construction, which in turn will be influenced by the type and amount of soil available:

1. Those constructed of impermeable soil throughout, i.e., homogeneous construction as illustrated in Fig. 5.
2. Those which are constructed of permeable soil with a core of impermeable soil, i.e., zoned and diaphragm construction as illustrated in Figs. 6 and 7.
3. Those which are constructed entirely of permeable soil with an impermeable surfacing on the wet slope, i.e., blanket construction as illustrated in Fig. 8.

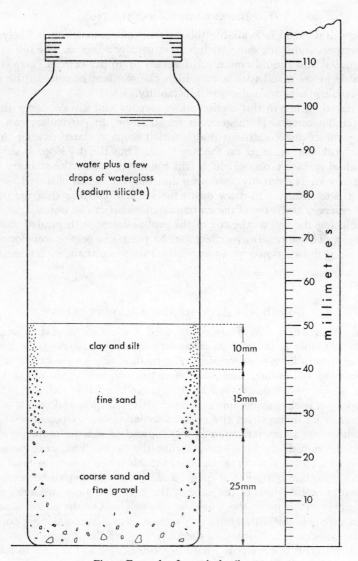

Fig. 4. Example of a typical soil test

Total depth of soil = 50 mm

Proportion of clay and silt = $\dfrac{10 \text{ mm}}{50 \text{ mm}} \times 100$ = 20 per cent

Proportion of fine sand = $\dfrac{15 \text{ mm}}{50 \text{ mm}} \times 100$ = 30 per cent

Proportion of coarse sand and fine gravel = $\dfrac{25 \text{ mm}}{50 \text{ mm}} \times 100$ = 50 per cent

Homogeneous Construction

Where suitable soil is available this method of construction is likely to be the cheapest and is the one which is most usually adopted. The soil must be well graded and should contain at least 20 to 30 per cent of clay. It is inadvisable to use a soil with a very high clay content because of the risk of excessive shrinkage and subsequent instability.

As stated earlier in this section some seepage will always occur through earth embankments. Homogeneous construction, in particular, can sometimes produce the conditions under which seepage water passing through the embankment emerges on the dry slope. Thus the dry slope is subjected to gradual surface erosion, which will eventually affect the stability of the embankment. The remedy, assuming that the rate of loss of stored water by seepage is tolerable, is to draw down the seepage paths so that the seepage water emerges at the toe of the embankment. This can be done, if necessary, by replacing the soil at the toe of the embankment with graded stone-fill, see Fig. 5. The same erosive effect can be produced on the wet slope if the reservoir is drawn down at an excessive rate more than, say, 1 metre per week.

Zoned and Diaphragm Construction

Zoned construction should always be used if a sufficient variety of soils is readily available because of its inherent advantages, particularly from the point of view of long-term stability. The method consists essentially of using impermeable soil to form a seepage barrier or core within the embankment, which is otherwise constructed of permeable but stable soil, see Fig. 6. If the supply of impermeable soil is sufficient, the cheapest and easiest solution is to construct as much of the embankment interior as possible with this soil, within the limits indicated in Fig. 6, and to use the more permeable soil on the outside to form and stabilize the slopes. The more permeable the soil which is used to form the core, the wider the core must be if it is to offer an adequate barrier to seepage. For soils containing 20 per cent to 30 per cent clay the width of the core at the base of the embankment should be about equal to twice the embankment height. On the other hand, if a limited supply of soil with a high clay content is available a thinner core wall may be constructed. Normally, the only form of diaphragm construction suitable for farm reservoirs is where bentonite-filled soil is used to form an impermeable wall within the embankment, which is otherwise constructed of permeable soil, see Fig. 7. This form of construction is further explained on page 50.

Blanket Construction

In the parts of the country where suitable impermeable soils are not available or only occur in very limited quantities, the embankment can be constructed of permeable soil with a waterproofing blanket on the wet slope, see Fig. 8. Suitable blanket materials would be good quality dense clay, PVC, polyethylene or butyl rubber. A clay blanket must be covered with at least 0·6 metres of other material to minimize the liability to cracking. PVC and polyethylene sheeting must also be protected with soil, see pages 48 and 49.

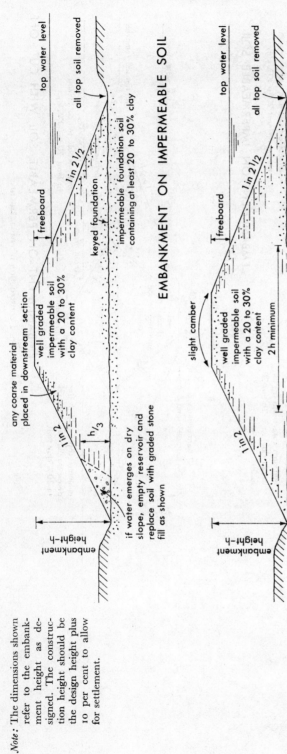

EMBANKMENT ON IMPERMEABLE SOIL

EMBANKMENT ON PERMEABLE SOIL WITH CUT-OFF

Fig. 5. Homogeneous construction of embankments

Note: The dimensions shown refer to the embankment height as designed. The construction height should be the design height plus 10 per cent to allow for settlement.

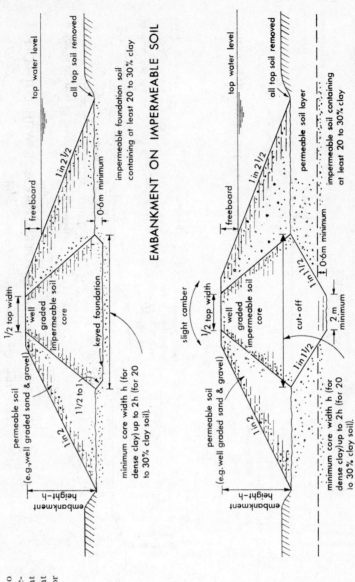

EMBANKMENT ON IMPERMEABLE SOIL

EMBANKMENT ON PERMEABLE SOIL WITH CUT-OFF

Fig. 6. Zoned construction of embankments

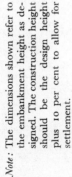

Note: The dimensions shown refer to the embankment height as designed. The construction height should be the design height plus 10 per cent to allow for settlement.

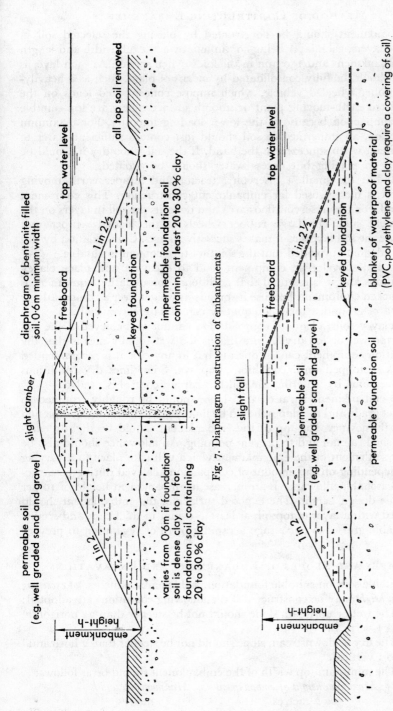

Fig. 7. Diaphragm construction of embankments

Fig. 8. Blanket construction of embankments

Note: The dimensions shown refer to the embankment height as designed. The construction height should be the design height plus 10 per cent to allow for settlement.

4B

METHOD OF CONSTRUCTING EMBANKMENTS

The embankment should be constructed by placing the selected soil in successive layers, each layer being continuous over the full width and length of the embankment and 150 mm in thickness when spread. As each layer is placed it should be fully consolidated by means of plant, such as a heavily-loaded rubber wheeled vehicle, which impose concentrated loads on the soil. Tracked earth-moving plant or smooth surface rollers are less suitable for soil compaction because of the lower loading intensity. For maximum consolidation, an impermeable soil should just contain sufficient water to remain intact when squeezed in the hand. If the soil is too dry it should be moistened on placing but excess water should be avoided.

For all but the smallest reservoirs, tractor and scraper earth moving equipment is mostly used for embankment construction. This equipment scrapes soil from the reservoir floor area and deposits the soil in layers on the embankment site. The large rubber wheels of the loaded scraper unit consolidate the soil layers as it makes successive passes. Consolidation by this means is adequate provided that the soil moisture content is suitable.

Bucket and shovel type equipment tend to excavate and place clayey soils in lumps and it is essential that additional consolidating equipment is used. Tracked equipment, because it spreads its weight over a comparatively large area of ground, cannot adequately consolidate clayey soils.

With clayey soils adequate consolidation cannot be achieved if the soil is either too wet or too dry. A site that is too wet usually means that the consolidation equipment cannot operate but in any case it is recommended that work is stopped until conditions improve. Sometimes dry conditions can be overcome by watering the soil but careful control is needed.

As the embankment is raised the slopes should be roughly trimmed to the correct grade and the slopes should be finally graded after the completion of all earth-moving. The top of the embankment should be slightly cambered to shed rainfall and to prevent ponding. An allowance should also be made for settlement of the embankment which will take place to a varying degree, depending on the amount of compaction achieved during construction. A reasonable allowance is an increase in embankment height of 10 per cent of the design height. The exposed surface of the embankment should be covered with a layer of topsoil, at least 150 mm in thickness, and seeded with suitable grasses to encourage a rapid growth of vegetation to prevent erosion.

SHAPES AND SLOPES OF EMBANKMENT AND EXCAVATIONS

Using suitable soils on suitable foundation, stable embankments *not exceeding 5 metres in height* may be constructed if the following conditions are adopted:

1. The wet or upstream slope should not be steeper than $2\frac{1}{2}$ horizontal to 1 vertical.
2. The dry or downstream slope should not be steeper than 2 horizontal to 1 vertical.
3. The minimum top width of the embankment should be as follows:

Maximum height of embankment	Minimum top width
2 metres	2·5 metres
3 metres	2·75 metres
4 metres	3·0 metres
5 metres	3·25 metres

Embankment with flatter slopes and wider top widths require larger quantities of soil and the embankments occupy more area, but such banks are easier to construct with heavy equipment. This is an important consideration as unit earth-moving costs could be lower, giving a better job for about the same total cost.

Small reservoir embankments constructed of non water-retaining soils, e.g., sands and gravels, and waterproofed on the wet slope with a blanket not requiring a soil cover may be built with slightly steeper slopes.

The side slopes of reservoirs, or parts of reservoirs, excavated below ground level should not be steeper than $2\frac{1}{2}$ horizontal to 1 vertical to ensure stability. Steeply sloping banks slip sooner or later and this may affect the stability of adjoining land and property, also the capacity of small reservoirs may be considerably reduced. Where embanking is to be carried out adjacent to excavated slopes to provide extra depth, the embankments should preferably be separated from the top edge of the excavation by a berm about 3 metres wide. This will increase the stability of the combined slopes and facilitates construction by providing a working space for excavating plant.

EMBANKMENT PROTECTION

Embankment and excavation slopes need to be protected from erosion caused by wave action on the wet slope and by weathering and rainfall on the top and exposed surfaces of both slopes. For wet slopes stone pitching or other hard materials provide the most durable protection but may not be cheaply available. Reinforced bituminous sheeting has also been used for this purpose. The growth of suitable vegetation, such as reeds or special grasses, gives a fair degree of protection. Strains of creeping bent and rough stalk meadow grass are probably the best grasses for this purpose; they flourish in wet or dry conditions and are comparatively low growing. The seeds are more expensive than farm grass seeds and the banks require covering with fine soil before sowing. Reeds, rushes and aquatic grass are effective but spread rapidly and their growth may get out of hand. Tree trunks or bundles of faggots anchored at the water-line will break up the wave action and prevent damage to the banks until such time as vegetation is properly established. The intersection of an impounding dam with the sides of the valley will form a drainage channel, and special measures may be necessary to prevent erosion at this point.

Earth embankments and other works, especially lined reservoirs, which are liable to damage by cattle or other stock, should be protected by stock-proof fencing. In most circumstances fencing is required to protect the public from the physical dangers of the reservoir itself and to comply with safety legislation.

RESERVOIR PIPEWORK

Reservoir pipework can be placed in two categories, i.e., that passing over embankments and that passing through embankments. Pipes passing over embankments need to be sufficiently flexible either at the joints or in the pipe itself to accommodate movement of the supporting soil as the embankment settles. On the other hand, pipes passing through embankments must not only be flexible but also strong enough to withstand the high loads produced by uneven settlement. It is prudent in the latter case to adopt the most suitable type of pipe, regardless of expense, because of the high cost of replacing or repairing a pipe that has failed. Whatever type of pipe is used the joints must be watertight.

The following pipes are commonly used in farm reservoir schemes:

Asbestos cement pipes

These pipes are rigid but a degree of flexibility is given to a pipeline as the joints incorporate rubber rings. They are not as strong as cast iron, spun iron or steel pipes but their high resistance to deterioration makes them a good choice where strength is not important. Water or soil containing excessive sulphates will corrode these pipes.

Cast and spun iron pipes

These pipes are rigid, but flexible joints are available and should be used. Their inherent strength and good resistance to deterioration make them suitable for use in all positions but their high cost usually limits their use to situations where the earth loading is high, e.g., the bottom outlet to an impounding reservoir. Protection against corrosion may be necessary in some aggressive soils, particularly around certain types of flexible joints.

Polyethylene pipes

These pipes are readily available in sizes up to 2 inches diameter and their flexibility at all temperatures makes them a good choice for pumping feeds to offstream reservoirs. They have a high resistance to deterioration.

Unplasticized PVC pipes

At normal temperatures these pipes are flexible, but not so flexible as polyethylene pipes. As the temperature decreases the flexibility reduces until the pipe becomes brittle. It is therefore inadvisable to use PVC pipes in exposed positions. They have a very high resistance to deterioration. Where the earth loading is high, granular bedding is usually required but this cannot be used where it would form a seepage path underneath an embankment. Special provisions must be made for bedding and backfilling UPVC pipes in such situations.

Spun concrete pipes

As these pipes are rigid flexible joints must be used. Their strength makes them suitable for use in any position, except where the water or soil has an excessive sulphate content. It is essential to use the correct class of pipe for a particular loading.

Steel pipes

The strength of steel and a degree of flexibility make them very suitable for use in all positions but their life is limited due to corrosion. Flexible joints are seldom necessary. All pipes should be protected from corrosion by galvanizing, bitumen coating or wrapping with inert material or other recognized methods. The protection should be of the highest standard if the pipes are buried.

Rectangular notch constructed of galvanized steel plate and angle iron

Proportioning weirs control the flow from the stream into the pumping sump. A floating pump (not shown) feeds the water to an offstream reservoir

PLATE I

Acknowledgment: F. R. Mackley

Two unlined offstream reservoirs for orchard irrigation. Filled by flow from tile drains

Acknowledgment: F. R. Mackley

A 1600 cubic metre impounding reservoir

PLATE II

The dam of a 22 500 cubic metre impounding reservoir. The spillway around the side of the dam is shown in the foreground

Acknowledgment: F. R. Mackley

The spillway to a 45 000 cubic metre impounding reservoir. The control section has been lined with blockwork to prevent erosion

PLATE III

Acknowledgment: F. R. Mackley

A seepage reservoir supplemented by surface water. The overflow is in the background

Acknowledgment: Butyl Products Ltd.

A 500 cubic metre butyl rubber lined reservoir with safety fencing

PLATE IV

Acknowledgment: Butyl Products Ltd.

Site jointing of prefabricated butyl rubber sheet

Acknowledgment: British Cellophane Ltd.

Laying a protective soil cover to a polythene lining. The top edge of the lining is anchored in a trench

PLATE V

Synthetic fibre sheeting laid over a PVC lining to stabilize the soil cover

Acknowledgment: MacRae Farms Ltd. and E. Rand and Sons (Engineering) Ltd.

The inlet and floating suction outlet to a butyl rubber lined reservoir

PLATE VI

Sinking a 600 millimetre diameter borehole 46 metres into Greensand, using the method of reversed circulation

Acknowledgment: Butyl Products Ltd.

Laying butyl rubber sheet lining on the floor of a reservoir

PLATE VII

The primary overflow and bottom outlet to a 27 000 cubic metre impounding reservoir. A galvanized steel ring prevents floating trash from entering the vertical pipe. The valve spindle operates the bottom outlet valve

Direct abstraction from a river, showing pump house and intake works

PLATE VIII

ANTI-SEEPAGE COLLARS

Any pipe passing through an embankment below top water level must have anti-seepage collars to prevent the internal erosion of soil by seepage flow along the outside of the pipe. These collars, which increase the length of the seepage path by about 50 per cent, are usually made of concrete at least 150 mm thick. They should have an effective diameter equal to 5 pipe diameters and should be spaced 10 pipe diameters apart measured along the line of the pipe. For larger pipes the number of collars can be increased to decrease the overall size. Where collars of bottom outlet pipes project above the embankment formation level special attention should be given to compaction of soil around the collars.

MAINTENANCE

Good maintenance is essential, and expenditure will be required every year to maintain the reservoir in good condition. Periodic inspections of the embankment are necessary. There will always be some leakage from an earth embankment but any significant increase should be investigated and remedied. Cracks may develop in earth banks in dry weather and these should be filled at once. Any settlement of the embankment which exceeds that allowed for should be made good immediately. Grassed spillways need particular care and attention and should be kept clear of debris and any damage repaired at once. As spillways are rarely in action they are apt to be forgotten but their effectiveness depends on proper maintenance. Earthworks are subject to constant change, which may eventually lead to deterioration and possible destruction if the maintenance has been inadequate. Most concrete work eventually needs repair. The undermining and settlement of the supporting soil, leading to partial collapse of minor concrete works, is the most likely trouble. All embankments should be carefully examined after a severe storm. The clearance of pipes and the operation of moving parts, such as valves and penstocks, is essential if these are to function properly when needed. It may be an advantage to use some stored water to spray the exposed slopes and tops of a clay soil embankment to prevent excessive cracking in a prolonged drought.

Watertightness and Waterproofing of Reservoirs

THE NEED FOR WATERTIGHTNESS

REFERENCE has already been made on page 40 to the methods used to prevent excessive seepage when dams or embankments are constructed of permeable soil or on permeable foundations, or both. These precautions are taken because of the possible danger to the stability of the embankment, but they may also be called for because of the water loss which would otherwise occur. Anti-seepage measures, however, add considerably to the cost and difficulty of reservoir construction, so that it is generally preferable to try to find a site which will retain water naturally and where suitable soil is available to construct a watertight embankment.

Providing the stability of the embankment is not involved it may be necessary to accept some seepage loss through the reservoir floor and embankment, so long as there is sufficient inflow of water to replace it. If water is not available to make good the loss at the right time then it may be necessary either to provide extra storage capacity to allow for the seepage loss or to consider some method of waterproofing to prevent the loss.

In situations where the only possible site is in permeable ground such as sand, gravel or chalk, then waterproofing may be justified provided that it is economic in relation to any other alternative scheme and the irrigation benefit expected. In such circumstances it pays to give the fullest consideration to the justification for and the calculation of the proposed reservoir capacity.

WATERPROOFING METHODS

Over the last two decades various methods and materials have been advocated and used for the waterproofing of irrigation reservoirs. There is now evidence to show that the more expensive methods appear to have the longest useful life but that in all cases there is a need to ensure good standards of workmanship. The method adopted will depend upon a number of factors but adequate site investigation is a necessary preliminary before adopting any particular system. This will involve some initial expenditure but a subsequent saving in the final cost of a scheme is more than likely.

SHEET LINING METHODS

LAYING SHEET LININGS

Thin sheet linings have no structural strength and rely on a continuous backing for support. Thus earthworks must be adequately consolidated and trimmed. Particular attention should be given to the proper consolidation of any trenches cut for the laying of the various drains which may be needed in the reservoir floor or embankment slopes. The lined area must be free from sharp stones and the lining should be laid on a layer of fine earth or sand or on an underlay of a synthetic fibre material. It is very important that the soil on which the lining is laid should be sterilized to prevent the possibility of weeds growing and penetrating the lining. Advice should be sought on the most effective weedkiller but in some cases a 5 per cent solution of sodium chlorate sprayed at 3 litres per square metre should be sufficient.

To prevent displacement and damage the top edges of the lining should be securely anchored by burying about 0·6 m of the lining in a trench 0·3 m wide by 0·3 m deep excavated in the top of the embankment. Care should be taken that this trench, which is usually excavated after the embankment has been shaped and consolidated, is at a sufficient distance from the top of the embankment inside slope to avoid instability. A sheet lining should be able to withstand the weight of a man wearing rubber boots and it is important that the lining should be laid with sufficient slack to avoid it coming under stress during its life. The manufacturer's instructions on laying procedures should be carefully followed.

In situations where the ground water table is liable to rise above the floor level of the reservoir, the possible effect on the lining when the water level in the reservoir is lower than the ground water level behind the lining must be considered. Although a soil treatment lining such as clay is likely to be disrupted under this condition, a flexible sheet lining will probably rise as the reservoir is emptied and settle back into position as the reservoir is filled. This is not possible, however, with sheet linings which require the laying of a soil cover on the embankment slopes. In such cases it may be necessary to lower the water table by the installation of a suitable drainage system.

The following are the more commonly used lining materials:

PVC SHEET LINING

Flexible PVC lining is made from plasticized polyvinyl chloride, a material which is chemically inert under most conditions. For reservoir lining it should not be less than 0·35 mm in thickness. Linings for small storage reservoirs can be purchased ready made in one piece. For larger reservoirs the suppliers will contract to provide and lay a lining complete, the sheets being laid and jointed on the site.

PVC lining tends to harden when exposed to sunlight, especially above the water-line, and it is then easily damaged. Thus PVC linings laid on the embankment slopes should be protected with a covering of soil at least 0·3 metres in thickness, and suitably graded to avoid damage to the lining. To ensure that the soil covering is stable, the slopes should not be steeper that 1 in 3, preferably 1 in 4, and where wave action is likely the slopes may need to be even flatter. The stability of the soil cover can sometimes be improved by using a synthetic fibre underlay to the soil cover laid on top of the lining. It is not essential to cover lining laid on the reservoir floor provided that at least 0·3 m of water is allowed to remain above the lining at all times.

PVC lining is one of the cheapest common methods of waterproofing a reservoir at the present time. Whilst life expectation is still somewhat uncertain, linings have been in satisfactory service for at least 10 years and a much longer effective life is claimed. The properties of plasticized PVC sheeting depend on its chemical composition, which can vary considerably. The main safeguard is to choose a supplier who has an established reputation for this type of work and also to ensure that the work on site is carried out to the best standards.

POLYETHYLENE SHEET LINING

Polyethylene sheeting (common name 'polythene') is another material which is chemically inert in most conditions. For reservoir linings it should not be less than 0·25 mm in thickness.

In general, the comments made above concerning PVC as a lining material apply to polyethylene and it is necessary to cover the lining with soil. Polyethylene has also been in use for this purpose for more than 10 years and its success depends largely on the quality of the material supplied and its correct installation.

BUTYL RUBBER SHEET LINING

Butyl rubber lining is made from synthetic rubber, a very versatile material which is resistant to sunlight and is chemically inert under most conditions. As in the case of PVC or polyethylene linings the properties of any particular make of butyl rubber lining depend upon its chemical composition. High grade butyl rubber has potentially a much better resistance to ageing than PVC or polyethylene and is superior in this respect to natural rubber.

The minimum thickness of butyl rubber lining used in farm reservoirs is 0·75 mm, but thicknesses of 1·00 mm and 1·50 mm are also standard. The lining can be fabricated by machine in the factory into the large sheets of the appropriate dimensions to fit a particular site, the limitation being the size and weight which can be off-loaded and handled with normal plant. The largest prefabricated area of sheeting is normally 30 m by 30 m (approximately a tonne in weight).

Jointing on site is by a process of hot vulcanization. Openings for pipes are provided in factory-made sleeves, which are bonded to the lining by a pressure tape.

There is no need to cover butyl rubber with soil.

SOIL TREATMENT METHODS

CLAY LINING

Although this is not a method which can be recommended with any confidence, as success is likely to be difficult and costly to achieve, clay linings have been used to waterproof reservoirs with varying results. The effectiveness of the lining depends upon the type of clay used, the standards of workmanship adopted and whether the lining forms a homogeneous sheet of clay of adequate thickness when consolidated. If the clay has to be brought from a distance the cost may be higher than the cost of sheet lining the reservoir. The type of clay used is important because reliance is placed on a relatively thin layer. Ideally the content of clay particles should be sufficiently high to prevent seepage but not so high that the soil will shrink or crack badly on drying out when the water level is low. This is very difficult to achieve. To reduce the liability to cracking, a clay lining should be covered with at least 0·6 metres of other soil, preferably sand or gravel on the embankment slope. A soil cover is not required on the reservoir floor provided that it is covered with at least 0·3 metres of water at all times. Extra care and attention should be given to site investigations, with an adequate number of trial holes sufficient to establish the nature and quantity of clay available for forming the lining. During construction the moisture content of the clay should be at the right level to secure easy digging, filling and compaction. Generally, this work is best carried out by using tractor and scraper earth-moving equipment with close supervision of the work at all stages.

TABLE 5

Cost of waterproofing earth reservoirs

The actual cost of waterproofing will depend upon the quantity of material involved and the location of the reservoir.
Descriptions of the various materials listed in the table are given above.

Material	Cost of material and laying per square metre
Butyl rubber, 0·75 mm thick	£2·60
PVC 0·35 mm thick (including soil cover)	£1·60
Polyethylene 0·25 mm thick (including soil cover)	£1·00
Synthetic fibre underlay	£0·60

CUT-OFF METHODS

This method, to which reference has already been made on page 37, can be used where the reservoir floor is permeable but an impermeable layer exists a short distance below the floor. In these conditions it may be possible to construct an impermeable barrier around the perimeter of the reservoir extending down to the impermeable layer, thereby achieving a watertight basin. The simplest version of this method is to excavate a trench down to the impermeable layer and to fill it with good quality clay, thoroughly packed in thin layers.

A development of this method, of which there is very limited experience in farm reservoirs, is to use a bentonite slurry to hold up a length of trench which is then backfilled with the originally excavated material, the interstices of which become filled with bentonite. Bentonite is a natural clay, usually supplied as dry powder in bags, which has the property of swelling and forming a thixotropic gel if mixed with water. Thus bentonite grains deposited in the pores of a soil and coming into contact with water will swell and increase the watertightness of the soil. The type of bentonite to be used depends upon the particular soil and task; low sodium bentonite, for example, breaks down in contact with chalk.

Other methods of using bentonite are for the waterproofing of bed and embankment surfaces by mixing bentonite powder with the soil and then compacting the mixture. An alternative is to cover a layer of bentonite laid on the surface to be waterproofed with a layer of soil.

The suppliers of the material should be consulted regarding the feasibility of using bentonite in any particular circumstance. Their advice needs to be carefully followed on the way the work is to be carried out. As bentonite is a comparatively new material for waterproofing earth reservoirs in this country it has not as yet been proved, although it is claimed to be extensively used in the USA.

Appendix A

BASES FOR THE DESIGN OF A TYPICAL IRRIGATION SCHEME

THE following example illustrates the design of a typical scheme. The information obtained at each stage of the design is summarized in Fig. 9. There are many decisions to be made in the course of designing a scheme to meet a particular irrigation requirement depending upon local circumstances and it is recommended that the services of a suitably experienced consultant should be obtained.

GENERAL CONSIDERATIONS

The example assumes that a farmer in eastern England wishes to irrigate main crop potatoes* on a sandy loam soil. A possible source of water on the farm is a small watercourse, which usually has a reasonable winter flow but the summer flow varies widely from year to year. Although little information is available at this stage it is assumed that perhaps the winter flow could provide an adequate but limited source of water. The Water Authority advises that an abstraction licence could be issued but that it would be conditional upon a specified residual flow being maintained in the watercourse downstream of the abstraction point at all times.

Because of the unreliability of summer flow, direct abstraction from the watercourse is not considered. There is also some doubt as to the advisability of adopting offstream storage filled by winter pumping because it would not be possible to ensure that all flow in excess of the residual flow is abstracted. This is considered to be necessary because of the limited amount of water probably available.

There are only two solutions to the problem of storing all flows in excess of the residual flow. The first to be considered is a gravity-fed offstream reservoir with a suitably designed inlet weir arrangement. Such a reservoir requires a reasonably level area in the vicinity of the watercourse and this is not available on the farm. The second is an impounding reservoir which, on the evidence available at this stage, seems a possible solution but further investigation is needed before a final decision could be made.

As the amount of water available from the watercourse in a dry year is unknown and as it would be unwise to proceed on this basis, a vee notch flow gauge is installed as described in Appendix D. Measurements of the flow in the watercourse are taken over the winter months as described in Appendix F and the probable dry winter flow determined as described in Appendix G. Although this exercise may delay the scheme it is the only safe way to proceed. To design and install an irrigation scheme without knowledge of how much water is likely to be available is inviting a costly failure.

As storage has been adopted a further decision is made, that the irrigation requirements should be based on the fifth driest year in 20 so as to reduce the

---

* Most schemes provide for the irrigation of several crops but the above is assumed for this simple example.

capacity and cost of the reservoir. This decision means that in years drier than the fifth driest year the amount of water available would not meet the requirements in these years, and it should be recognized that gross margins may be restricted. Whether to design for the drier years is a matter of comparing the extra cost with the extra benefit.

IRRIGATION REQUIREMENTS

The crops to be irrigated are listed in Section 2 of Fig. 9, in this case 10 hectares of maincrop potatoes. It is decided that an appropriate irrigation plan for a sandy loam soil is to apply 38 mm of water when the soil moisture deficit reaches 38 mm during the accepted crop response period of June to August. Maps of long-term irrigation need, which are available to the local ADAS adviser, indicate that a seasonal total of 160 mm of water is required in the fifth driest year in 20 years. In confirmation of the previous decision to adopt the fifth driest year, it is noted that the total water requirement to meet the irrigation need in the driest year in 20 years is 250 mm, i.e., an increase of about 50 per cent, which would considerably increase the cost of the scheme.

IRRIGATION EQUIPMENT

The information in Section 3 of Fig. 9 is based on the characteristics of the irrigation equipment to be adopted. After considering the full range of commercial equipment available it is decided to adopt equipment which can apply 5 mm per hour of water over an irrigation cycle of 15 days, which conforms to the adopted irrigation plan described above.

To restore the soil moisture deficit to zero when it has reached 38 mm at a rate of 5 mm per hour requires an application time of 7·5 hours. Over a 15 hour working day there will be two settings of the equipment and 30 settings will be needed over an irrigation cycle of 15 days. The nominal area of irrigation equipment required for one setting is the total crop area of 10 hectares divided by 30 settings, i.e., 0·33 hectares.

The remainder of the information in Section 3 of Fig. 9 can be obtained from the equipment manufacturers but it can also be calculated. If the sprinkler spacing is a nominal 18 m, a total of 10 sprinklers are required to cover 0·33 hectares (3300 m²) and an application of 5 mm per hour over an area of 18 × 18 square metres is equivalent to a single sprinkler output of nearly 0·5 litres per second. Thus the total output is 5 litres per second and the daily quantity required is 270 cubic metres.

WATER REQUIREMENTS

The information given in Sections 2 and 3 of Fig. 9 is summarized in Section 4.

WATER SOURCE

Gauging of the watercourses over the winter six months indicates that the total winter runoff was 10 500 hectare millimetres. The catchment area of the watercourse is determined as described below and is found to be 100 hectares. Thus the equivalent runoff in that winter is 105 mm and the probable dry winter runoff is 32 mm, i.e., an average probable dry winter stream flow of 2 litres per second. The probable total dry winter runoff is

32 000 cubic metres, which exceeds the seasonal irrigation requirement by a comfortable margin, assuming that most of the water can be put to irrigation use. This information is summarized in Section 5 of Fig. 9.

CATCHMENT AREA

A method of determining the boundary of a catchment area is by inspection of the appropriate 1 in 25 000 contoured Ordnance Survey maps. On these maps the contours are coloured brown and if successive increasing contour lines are followed up the valley side slopes and bed slope from the point of abstraction or storage until points are reached at which the contours begin to decrease into the next valley, then a line joining these points can form a reasonable estimate of the catchment boundary. The catchment area can be roughly estimated by comparing the area within this boundary with the area contained within the grid lines on the map, which is 100 hectares. A more accurate figure can be obtained by drawing a 1 cm square grid on a piece of transparent paper and placing this over the catchment area as drawn on the map and counting the number of 1 cm squares within the area. The number of squares multiplied by 6·25 is the catchment area in hectares.

STORAGE

As described above it is considered that an impounding reservoir is a possible solution. The nett capacity of the reservoir should be 16 000 cubic metres if the irrigation design requirements are to be met. Knowing the nett capacity, the next step is to find out whether the valley of the water-course can accept a reservoir of this size. A site survey using a hand level indicates that the average valley bed slope is 1 in 50 and the average valley side slope is 1 in 20. Using this information in Fig. 17 shows that the actual capacity required to provide 16 000 cubic metres of irrigation water is 25 000 cubic metres. The corresponding maximum height of the dam is 4·6 metres (see page 26), which is reasonable for farm construction. The water to earth ratio from Fig. 18 is 6·6 and thus the volume of the dam and also the volume of the soil removed from behind the dam is about 4000 cubic metres.

Trial holes on the site indicate that there is a considerable depth of clay loam soil which, using the test explained on page 38, is shown to contain 35 per cent clay. This is suitable for homogeneous construction of the dam, see page 40.

SIZE OF SPILLWAY AND PRIMARY OVERFLOW

An investigation is made of the valley for a considerable distance downstream of the proposed site, including areas well outside the farm boundary, and it is concluded that there would be no significant damage to property or any risk of loss of life downstream if the dam failed. It is therefore decided that it would be reasonable to adopt the recommendations in this Bulletin regarding the spillway size and design.

To determine the size of spillway from Figs. 2 and 3, information on the average catchment slope, average annual rainfall and catchment area is required. The average catchment slope is best determined by inspection of a 1 in 25 000 contoured Ordnance Survey map of the area. The watercourse is followed up the valley from the dam site until the catchment boundary, as determined above, is reached. The horizontal distance from the reservoir site to the boundary is measured on the map and is found to be 2000 metres. (1 cm on a 1 in 25 000 map is 250 m on the ground.) The rise in ground level from the site to the boundary is also obtained from the map by inspection of the contour lines and is found to be about 20 metres. Thus the average catchment slope is 2000 divided by 20, i.e., 1 in 100. The catchment area is 100 hectares, determined as described previously.

The Meteorological Office states that the average annual rainfall for the area is 800 mm.

Using this information in Fig. 2 gives a spillway capacity of 1·6 cumecs and Fig. 3 gives a spillway width of 4 m. A spillway of this dimension can be accommodated in undisturbed ground around the side of the dam.

The primary overflow capacity is 25 per cent of 1·6 cumecs, i.e., 0·4 cumecs and Table 4 indicates that an overflow weir of 1·3 metres is required.

This information is summarized in Section 6 of Fig. 9.

On the information now available a final decision is made that an impounding reservoir can provide the required storage capacity and is the best solution.

ABSTRACTION LICENCE

The farmer applies for and is issued with a combined abstraction and impounding licence.

The licence specifies that the watercourse can be impounded to contain not more than 30 000 cubic metres of water; that the total annual abstraction must not exceed 20 000 cubic metres; that the maximum daily abstraction must not exceed 300 cubic metres and that a residual flow of 0·5 litres per second must be maintained in the watercourse downstream of the dam at all times.

COMPENSATION FLOW

To achieve the required residual flow a bottom outlet pipe underneath the dam is required and the most convenient arrangement is a combined bottom outlet and primary overflow, as illustrated in Fig. 24.

To demonstrate that 0·5 litres per second is being maintained downstream at all times requires an arrangement which the Water Authority may specify in the licence. One method is to construct a vee notch in the watercourse just downstream of the dam and adjust the flow from the reservoir by means of the bottom outlet valve until there is a depth of water flowing through the notch corresponding to a flow of 0·5 litres per second. Appendix D indicates that the depth or head over the notch should be just over 40 mm.

PUMPING PLANT

The pumping plant described in Section 7, Fig. 9 is either for filling a reservoir or for providing a supply to feed the irrigation equipment or both.

In this case the pump is required to feed the irrigation equipment. The nominal output for the scheme is 5 litres per second but it is decided that provision should be made for a limited future expansion of the scheme and a pump capable of delivering 7 litres per second is selected. The required pumping head is a combination of the total vertical lift, the friction loss

1. Name and Address
   of designer of project
   Tel. No.

2. CROPS TO BE IRRIGATED

   Please show any crops already irrigated first, and then the additional crops to be irrigated under the present proposals.

Crop	Area (ha)	Outdoor or glass	Depth (mm) of water per season	Which months under irrigation
Main crop	10	Outdoor	160 mm	June to
potatoes			(38 mm at	August
			38 mm SMD	
			5th driest	
			year)	

3. SPRAY EQUIPMENT

   (a) Type _____ 　　　(b) Max. no. of nozzles in simultaneous use ___10___

   (c) Output per nozzle ___0.5___ litre/s 　(d) Max. demand (b) x (c) ___5___ litre/s

   (e) Spraying hours per day ___15___ 　　(f) Spraying days per month ___30___

4. WATER REQUIREMENTS — SUMMARY

	Litre/s *	m^3/day*	m^3/year
Present water requirements	────	────	────
Additional water requirements	5	270	16 000
Total water requirements	5	270	16 000

   *based on the actual spray equipment to be used

5. WATER SOURCE (description — complete (a), (b) or (c) as necessary)

   (a) Surface (watercourse, ~~ditch, canal, lake or pond~~)

   　　(i) Contributary catchment ___100___ ha

   　　(ii) Estimated reliable dry ~~weather~~ winter flow ___2___ litre/s

   (b) Ground water (borehole, well, spring, seepage hole, gravel pit, etc.): Estimated yield _____ litre/s

   (c) Public main: Estimated available flow _____ litre/s

   (d) Give source of estimate in (a), (b) or (c) above:-

   　　Watercourse gauged over winter months and total flow adjusted to estimate probable dry winter-flow

   　　　　Combined abstraction and 　　maximum storage 30 000 m^3
   　　　　impounding licence 　　　　maximum annual abstraction 20 000 m^3
   　　　　　　　　　　　　　　　　maximum daily abstraction 300 m^3
   　　　　　　　　　　　　　　　　residual flow 0.5 litre/s

   (e) Is the quality of the water known to be suitable for irrigation? ___Yes___

   (f) Is it intended now or in the future to irrigate any crop of which the part exposed to the air is to be eaten raw? ___No___

Fig. 9A. Bases for the design of a typical irrigation scheme

6. STORAGE PROPOSED
    (a) Why is storage needed?   direct abstraction from watercourse not permitted
    (b) Type (delete where not applicable)
        earth: state whether impounding/off-stream — gravity/pumped supply
        concrete: brick: steel: cast iron:
    (c) Capacity ____ 25 000 ____ m³
    (d) Capacity above natural ground level ____ 21 000 ____ m³
    (e) Description of earth embankment(s), including maximum height, top width, earth slopes and freeboard:-
    (f) Excavation _____ 4000 _____ m³   maximum height 4.6 m
                                                      top width 3.5 m
                                                      inside slope 1 in 2.5
                                                      outside slope 1 in 2
                                                      freeboard 0.9 m
    (g) Estimated peak run-off ____ 1.6 ____ m³/s
    (h) Total peak run-off to storage ____ 1.6 ____ m³/s
    (i) Capacity of storm overflow ____ 1.6 ____ m³/s
    (j) Capacity of normal overflow ____ 0.4 ____ m³/s
    (k) Method of controlling overflow:-

        combined primary overflow and bottom outlet
        spillway discharges across valley slope into the watercourse

    (l) Soil investigation
        (i) Number of trial holes ____ 5 ____ depth ____ 4 ____ m
        (ii) Description of strata:-

    (m) Details of lining (if any):-

	Material	Thickness (mm)
Lining		
Covering to lining		

        None

7. PUMPING PLANT
    (a) Requirement: (i) Output at rated duty ____ 5 ____ litre/s
                          (ii) Total head (all causes) at rated output ____ 70 ____ m head.
                          (iii) Pumping time ____ 15 ____ hours/day
    (b) Proposed pump(s): (i) No. of pumps ____ 1 ____ Make ____
                          (ii) Type   two stage centrifugal
                          (iii) Rated performance (each pump) ____ 7 ____ litre/s at ____ 80 ____ m head at ____ 2900 ____ rev/min
                          (iv) Maximum pressure ____ 10 ____ bar
    (c) Prime mover: (permanent/portable/electric/
                          internal combustion engine/tractor)* Rating ____ 11 ____ kW at ____ 2900 ____ rev/min
    (d) Pump house: (timber/brick/concrete/other)* Size ____ 2 ____ m long by ____ 1 ____ m wide
    (e) Electrical supply: (overhead/underground)* Distance ____ 100 ____ m ____ 440 ____ volts ____ 3 ____ phase
    *Delete where not applicable.

8. PIPE LINE DESIGN

    (a) Total water demand of equipment ____ 5 ____ litre/s
    (b) Water level at source ____ 20 ____ m AOD (lowest reservoir level)
    (c) Maximum ground level to be reached ____ 80 ____ m AOD
    (d) Ground level at pump ____ 25 ____ m AOD
    (e) Ground level at lowest point of pipe system ____ 25 ____ m AOD

Fig. 9B. Bases for the design of a typical irrigation scheme

through the permanent and portable pipework, the losses due to pipe fittings, and the residual head required at the nozzles to operate the equipment. This is a technical problem on which advice may need to be sought.

For this example the total pumping head is assumed to be 70 metres.

A 3 phase 440V electricity supply is available near to the site and it is decided to adopt a permanent electrically powered pumping set housed in a small prefabricated concrete building. The pump selected can deliver 7 litres per second against a head of 80 metres at 2900 rpm. The maximum pressure is the pressure which can be developed by the pump under closed valve conditions, i.e., no pipe flow, and the manufacturers literature indicates that this is 10 bar, (1 bar is equal to the standard atmospheric pressure, which is approximately equal to 10 metres head of water). The maximum pressure determines what pressure class of pipe should be adopted.

The information on the pumping plant is summarized in Section 7, Fig. 9.

Detailed Design

The information obtained above should be sufficient to enable the detailed design of the scheme to proceed and accurate costings to be made.

Appendix B

WATER QUALITY

THE chemical and bacteriological quality of water may affect its suitability for irrigation. Some pollution can be tolerated but the difficulty is to determine the degree of pollution and to define a permissible amount. Further assistance can be obtained from the local ADAS adviser.

CHEMICAL QUALITY

Some chemical substances, e.g., sodium chloride (common salt), if present in sufficient amounts, may have a damaging effect on crop growth, soils and irrigation equipment.

Effect on crop growth

Water from boreholes or springs may contain large amounts of dissolved salts which are harmful to crop growth. Brackish water containing an amount of sodium chloride in excess of 500 milligrams per litre should not be used for irrigation. River water, sewage or other polluted water containing salts of certain metals, e.g., chromium, zinc, aluminium or copper may have a deleterious effect on crops. Experiments have shown that irrigating with water containing detergents can adversely affect plant growth, but with a few obvious exceptions natural river waters generally in this country have not yet been found to contain sufficient concentration of detergents to have any significant effect when used for ordinary irrigation.

Effect on crop value

Water containing appreciable quantities of iron compounds may stain market garden and salad crops a brown-reddish colour to an extent which may make them unmarketable. This problem can occur in borehole supplies from sand formations. Iron compounds can be removed from the water but the necessary equipment is costly.

Effect on soils

Detergents can reduce the water-holding capacity of soils, but again the amounts in British rivers are not usually enough to cause much damage.

Effect on animal health

Poisoning of livestock has occurred from drinking water polluted by a wide variety of chemicals, usually from industrial effluents. But this is an uncommon hazard nowadays owing to strict control on the discharge of effluents. In most cases accessible pools of polluted water would present a greater risk than the irrigated crop itself.

Effect on irrigation systems

Chemical effect on non-ferrous pipe systems is comparatively rare. If the water is suitable for use on crops it is probable that it will not affect asbestos

59

cement, plastics or aluminium pipes. Water containing traces of copper, however, will have a corrosive effect on aluminium equipment. River water containing detergents has been known to wash out the lubricants from irrigation oscillators and pumps. Very soft waters tend to be acid in character and corrosive to steel pipes and fittings. Galvanizing is some protection but will not withstand the effect of strongly acid water. This aspect is less important now that plastics pipes are available.

An undue amount of suspended solids in the water will necessitate frequent cleaning of, the filters and nozzles. If the solids are abrasive, e.g., sand in borehole water, they will cause excessive wear to the moving parts of the equipment, e.g., pumps, oscillators, etc.

BACTERIOLOGICAL QUALITY

A hazard to health may arise from the use of polluted river water, sewage effluent or crude sewage for irrigation.

Crops

The greatest risk lies, possibly, with market garden and salad crops which are normally eaten raw. It arises when such crops are marketed too soon after irrigation with polluted river water and particularly where they have not been properly washed. To minimize the risk, irrigation should cease well before harvesting. Where some pollution of the water source is known to occur, treatment of the water may be necessary. This may involve the installation of chlorinating equipment and the washing of the produce with clean water.

Grassland

There is a remote but possible danger of pathogenic or other harmful bacteria being transmitted to milk by superficial contamination of the dairy cattle from grass recently irrigated with polluted water. It may, therefore, be advisable not to graze the field for at least a few days after irrigation. It is essential that the cows' udders are thoroughly cleansed before milking.

The use of river or other water containing sewage or sewage effluent for the irrigation of pasture or for water supply does not appear to be harmful to animals unless the sewage contains the causal organisms of infectious diseases to which they are susceptible. Thus any possible ill-effects from the use of polluted river or other water for irrigation will depend on the type and degree of pollution present. Crude or imperfectly treated sewage may contain pathogenic organisms or the eggs of the tapeworm *Taenia saginata*, of which the intermediate (cystic) stage is found in the flesh of cattle. There is reason is believe that the eggs of this tapeworm can pass unharmed through many existing sewage works.

Water used in glasshouses

The water used in glasshouses should be free from injurious chemicals and uncontaminated with organisms likely to be harmful to plants. The environment inside a glasshouse is conducive to the rapid multiplication of organisms, thus the water used need to be of a higher quality than for outside irrigation. Water of public supply quality should be used where possible.

Appendix C

CAPITAL COSTS OF SOURCE WORKS FOR IRRIGATION SCHEMES

FOR a particular irrigation scheme one or more of the following source works may be needed, unless the full amount of water required is always available from a surface source:

Borehole and ancillary works
Reservoir and ancillary works

The amount of capital expenditure needed for the construction of source works is highly variable, doubling or even trebling the total cost compared with a scheme where source works are not required. The costs quoted are based upon average current costs, but site circumstances vary so widely that the cost of any particular scheme may differ considerably.

The permanent elements of an approved irrigation scheme, including source works, are eligible for grant. Further information on the grants available can be obtained from the local ADAS adviser.

BOREHOLES

The cost of sinking a borehole depends upon the depth, diameter, type of strata encountered, extent of lining, need for screens, duration of testing and standards of the contractor employed. The testing, for example, can cost as much as the borehole. There is also the possibility that more than one borehole may have to be sunk and occasionally a satisfactory supply cannot be found. Under normal conditions a 300 mm diameter borehole may cost between £20-£55 per metre depth, but where circumstances are more difficult the cost may be even higher.

There is an additional cost for the pumping equipment necessary to abstract the water. Borehole pumps are likely to cost at least £1200 including installation if used to pump directly into the distribution system, but high capacity submersible pumps may cost as much as £3500 or more. If the water is to be pumped into storage the cost will be lower, because of the reduced output and lift, but another pump is needed to feed the water from storage into the distribution system.

EARTH RESERVOIRS

Construction

Earth reservoirs, even for a given capacity, vary widely in cost depending upon the following factors: type of reservoir, i.e., impounding or offstream; the volume of earth that has to be moved; the extent of overflow works;

61

the inlet and outlet arrangements and the standards of design and workmanship. The following costs for unlined offstream reservoirs up to 25 000 cubic metres are based on past irrigation schemes and include for all ancillary work except pumping, and provide a very general guide:

Water to earth ratio	Approximate capital costs
2 : 1	£0·45 per cubic metre of water stored
3 : 1	£0·3 per cubic metre of water stored

Waterproofing

The cost of waterproofing an earth reservoir is an additional expense necessary where suitable soil is not available. The cost will depend upon the size and depth of the reservoir and the type of waterproofing used. The approximate cost, assuming that the perimeter of the reservoir is known, is given by the expression

$$£ \frac{P \times P \times X}{16}$$

where   P = reservoir perimeter in metres, see Appendix K, Fig. 14
        X = cost of waterproofing in £ per square metre, see Table 6

Pumping

The capital cost of pumping equipment required to transfer water from a surface source to a reservoir depends upon the required rate of pumping and the operating head. A typical range of cost would be:

Operating head	Pump capacity	Cost
10 m	4–12 litre/s	£500–£2000

Ancillary works, such as the construction of a pump house, the supply of electricity and the provision of pipework, will involve additional expenditure.

EXAMPLE OF THE COSTS OF A PUMP-FED OFFSTREAM RESERVOIR AND DISTRIBUTION SYSTEM

A typical irrigation scheme requires 1600 ha mm of water to meet the seasonal demand in a dry summer. A watercourse convenient to the irrigated area is gauged and the amount of water available is found to be insufficient in a dry summer but sufficient in a dry winter. Thus a reservoir of 16 000 m³ nett capacity is needed to store the stream flow over the winter months. To allow for seepage and evaporation the capacity of the reservoir is increased to 18 000 m³. After considering all the relevant factors it is found that the most convenient form of storage is from a pump-fed offstream reservoir. The pump output head of 10 m is determined by the location of the pump and the reservoir and assuming an operating period of 1000 hours through the winter months a pump capacity of 18 m³/hr or 5 litre/s is required. The capital cost of the scheme is estimated below.

Capital cost of the reservoir at £0.3 per m³ = £5400 (3 : 1 water to earth ratio)

Capital cost of pump and ancillary work   = £1800

Capital cost of a pumped distribution system
    for 10 ha   = 2000 (based on a typical cost of £200 per irrigated hectare)

_____

Estimated total capital cost of scheme   £9200

_____

Appendix D

90° VEE NOTCH FLOW GAUGE

HEAD AND FLOW READINGS

Flow $= 1336\, h^{2\cdot48}$ litre/second

$\quad\quad\quad = 11\,549\, h^{2\cdot48}$ ha mm per day

where h = head over notch in metres

TABLE 6

Head in mm	litre/sec	ha mm per day
10	0·02	0·13
20	0·08	0·71
30	0·22	1·93
40	0·46	3·94
50	0·79	6·85
60	1·25	10·8
70	1·83	15·8
80	2·54	22·0
90	3·41	29·5
100	4·42	38·2
110	5·60	48·4
120	6·95	60·1
130	8·48	73·3
140	10·2	88·1
150	12·1	105
160	14·2	123
170	16·5	143
180	19·0	164
190	21·7	188
200	24·7	213
210	27·9	241
220	31·3	270
230	34·9	302
240	38·8	335
250	42·9	371
300	67·5	583

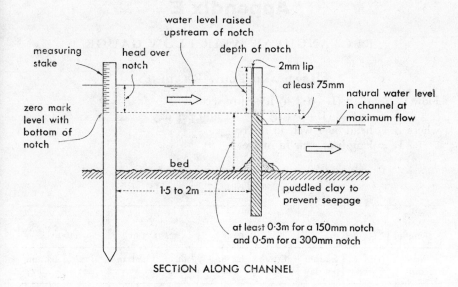

water level raised
upstream of notch

measuring
stake

head over
notch

depth of notch

2mm lip

at least 75mm

zero mark
level with
bottom of
notch

natural water level
in channel at
maximum flow

bed

1·5 to 2m

puddled clay to
prevent seepage

at least 0·3m for a 150mm notch
and 0·5m for a 300mm notch

SECTION ALONG CHANNEL

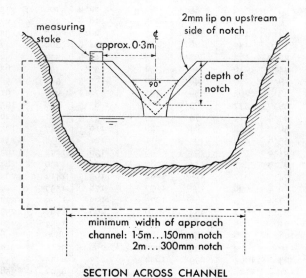

measuring
stake

2mm lip on upstream
side of notch

approx. 0·3m

90°

depth of
notch

minimum width of approach
channel: 1·5m...150mm notch
        2m... 300mm notch

SECTION ACROSS CHANNEL

Fig. 10. Installation of 90° vee notch flow gauge

Appendix E

RECTANGULAR WEIR FLOW GAUGE

Head and Flow Readings

Flow $= 1817 \, (L-0 \cdot 1 \, h) \, h^{1 \cdot 5}$ litre/second

$\quad\quad = 15\,698 \, (L-0 \cdot 1 \, h) \, h^{1 \cdot 5}$ ha mm per day

where h $=$ head over weir in metres

$\quad\quad$ L $=$ length of weir in metres

Table 7

Weir length	0·6 m		1·0 m		1·3 m		1·6 m	
head mm	litre/sec	ha mm per day	litre/sec	ha mm/day	litre/sec	ha mm/day	litre/sec	ha mm/day
20	3·07	26·5	5·13	44·3	6·67	57·6	8·21	70·9
30	5·64	48·7	9·41	81·3	12·2	106	15·1	130
40	8·66	74·8	14·5	125	18·8	163	23·2	200
50	12·1	104	20·2	175	26·3	227	32·4	280
60	15·9	137	26·5	229	34·6	299	42·6	368
70	20·0	172	33·4	289	43·5	376	53·6	463
80	24·3	210	40·8	352	53·1	459	65·5	565
90	29·0	250	48·6	420	63·3	547	78·1	674
100	33·9	293	56·9	491	74·1	640	91·4	789
110	39·0	337	65·6	566	85·5	738	105	910
120	44·4	384	74·6	645	97·3	841	120	1036
130	50·0	432	84·1	726	110	947	135	1168
140	55·8	482	93·9	811	122	1058	151	1304
150	61·8	534	104	898	136	1172	167	1446
160	67·9	587	114	989	149	1290	184	1592
170	74·3	642	125	1082	163	1412	202	1742
180	80·8	698	136	1177	178	1537	220	1897
190	87·4	755	148	1275	193	1666	238	2056
200	94·3	814	159	1376	208	1797	257	2219
210	101	875	171	1479	224	1932	276	2386
220	108	936	183	1584	240	2070	296	2556
230	116	999	196	1692	256	2211	316	2731
240	123	1063	209	1802	273	2355	337	2909
250	131	1128	221	1913	290	2502	358	3091
300	170	1470	290	2502	379	3276	469	4050

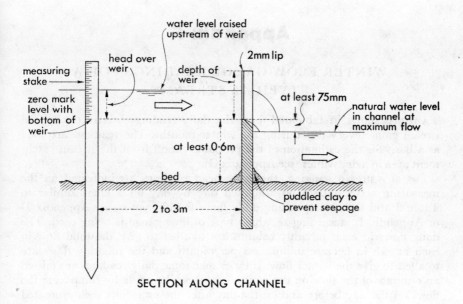

SECTION ALONG CHANNEL

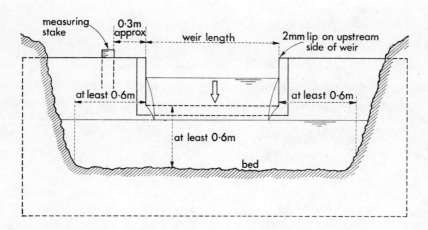

SECTION ACROSS CHANNEL

Fig. 11. Installation of a rectangular weir flow gauge

Appendix F

WINTER FLOW GAUGE READINGS FOR A TYPICAL STREAM

TABLE 8 shows in tabulated form the daily readings taken at a typical stream gauge every day during the winter months. The readings are used as a basis for the estimation of the probable runoff from the stream catchment area in a dry winter (see Appendix G).

For any stream gauging, the daily head readings, as indicated on the measuring stake, should be tabulated day by day on a chart similar to Table 8 and the corresponding daily flows found from either Appendix D or Appendix E, according to which type of flow gauge is being used. The daily flows in each monthly column are totalled to give the total flow in each month in hectare millimetres per month and the monthly flows are totalled to give the winter flow. If by chance some daily readings are missed an estimate of the flow on the omitted days can be made by comparing the flows on the day before and on the day after the omission; such estimated flows are shown in brackets in Table 8. Heads, as indicated on the measuring stake, should be read to the nearest 10 millimetres up or down, and any heads less than 10 millimetres shown as zero.

TABLE 8

Head measured in millimetres and daily flow measured in hectare millimetres per day, using a 90° vee notch

	October		November		December		January		February		March	
Day	Head	Flow	Head	Flow	Head	Flow	Head	Flow	Head	Flow	Head	Flow
1	60	10·8	60	10·8	90	29·5	80	22·0	80	22·0	70	15·8
2	70	15·8	60	10·8	90	29·5	90	29·5	80	22·0	70	15·8
3	60	10·8	70	15·8	—	(29·5)	90	29·5	60	10·8	80	22·0
4	50	6·9	70	15·8	90	29·5	100	38·2	70	15·8	—	22·0
5	50	6·9	60	10·8	90	29·5	110	48·4	70	15·8	80	22·0
6	80	22·0	70	15·8	70	15·8	120	60·1	—	(15·8)	70	15·8
7	90	29·5	80	22·0	—	(15·8)	120	60·1	—	(15·8)	70	15·8
8	80	22·0	60	10·8	70	15·8	130	73·3	70	15·8	60	10·8
9	—	(22·0)	60	10·8	80	22·0	130	73·3	80	22·0	70	15·8
10	80	22·0	60	10·8	80	22·0	130	73·3	90	29·5	80	22·0
11	60	10·8	50	10·8	80	22·0	130	73·3	90	29·5	90	29·5
12	60	10·8	50	10·8	90	29·5	130	73·3	90	29·5	—	(29·5)
13	50	6·9	40	3·9	90	29·5	130	73·3	100	38·2	90	29·5
14	50	6·9	50	6·9	90	29·5	130	73·3	100	38·2	100	38·2
15	70	15·8	60	10·8	90	29·5	120	60·1	100	38·2	100	38·2
16	80	22·0	70	15·8	100	38·2	120	60·1	90	29·5	—	(38·2)
17	60	10·8	80	22·0	100	38·2	130	73·3	90	29·5	100	38·2
18	50	6·9	80	22·0	100	38·2	—	(73·3)	—	(22·0)	100	38·2
19	50	6·9	70	15·8	100	38·2	—	(73·3)	80	22·0	90	29·5
20	60	10·8	70	15·8	90	29·5	—	(73·3)	70	15·8	90	29·5
21	60	10·8	70	15·8	—	(29·5)	130	73·3	100	38·2	80	22·0
22	50	6·9	70	15·8	90	29·5	120	60·1	100	38·2	80	22·0
23	50	6·9	60	10·8	80	22·0	120	60·1	80	22·0	80	22·0
24	50	6·9	60	10·8	80	22·0	120	60·1	80	22·0	—	(29·5)
25	50	6·9	60	10·8	80	22·0	110	48·4	70	15·8	90	29·5
26	70	15·8	70	15·8	70	15·8	110	48·4	90	29·5	70	15·8
27	40	3·9	70	15·8	70	15·8	100	38·2	90	29·5	70	15·8
28	50	6·9	70	15·8	70	15·8	90	29·5	90	29·5	60	10·8
29	50	6·9	80	22·0	70	15·8	90	29·5	—	—	60	10·8
30	50	6·9	90	29·5	80	22·0	80	22·0	—	—	70	15·8
31	40	3·9	—	—	80	22·0	80	22·0	—	—	90	29·5
		360·0		447·5		793·4		1705·9		702·4		739·8

Monthly totals: Hectare millimetres per month

Total winter flow = sum of monthly flows
= 4749 hectare millimetres
Catchment area assessed at 40 hectares

Therefore catchment runoff $= \dfrac{4749}{40} = 119$ millimetres

6

Appendix G

ESTIMATION OF STREAM FLOW IN A DRY WINTER

If the flow in a stream in any winter is known (see example at Appendix F) then the flow in the same stream in the driest winter in 20 can be estimated in the following manner. The method described should only be used when more sophisticated hydrological methods are not available to the reader. As with all simple empirical methods the results can in some cases differ from reality by an appreciable amount and if the calculated dry winter flow does not exceed the amount of water required by the irrigation system by a sufficient margin then alternative sources should be investigated.

To calculate the dry winter flow the following information is required:

gauged stream flow in any winter

rainfall in that winter
average winter rainfall   available from the Meteorological Office
rainfall in previous summer   or ADAS for the area concerned.
average summer rainfall

The method is based on the assumption that the winter rainfall and runoff have a simple relationship if the rainfall in the previous summer is equal to the summer average. This relationship, once established, can be used to estimate the dry winter runoff. Thus the calculations involve two adjustments to the actual gauged winter runoff. The first adjusts for the rainfall occurring in the previous summer, producing a corrected winter runoff based on the average summer rainfall. The second adjusts the corrected winter runoff to give an estimate of the runoff occurring in the driest winter in twenty. An error, which tends to over-estimate the dry winter runoff, will be introduced if storm flows form a large proportion of the total winter runoff, but for streams which are gauged once a day, it is likely that most storm flows will be missed.

The following example illustrates a typical calculation:

Information available:

Gauged runoff in a winter	=119 millimetres (from Appendix F)
Rainfall in that winter	=361 millimetres
Average winter rainfall	=297 millimetres
Rainfall in the previous summer	=343 millimetres
Average summer rainfall	=290 millimetres

1st Adjustment

The 'surplus' or 'deficit' of the rainfall in the previous summer is 'rainfall in previous summer' minus 'average summer rainfall':

= 343–290 millimetres
=+53 millimetres

Therefore there is a 'surplus' of 53 millimetres of summer rainfall. If the summer rainfall had been below average the answer would have been a 'deficit' with a negative (−) sign.

The proportion of the summer rainfall 'surplus' or 'deficit' which influences the winter runoff is:

$$\frac{\text{surplus}}{\text{or deficit}} \times \frac{\text{gauged winter runoff}}{\text{winter rainfall}} \times 2$$

$$= +53 \times \frac{119}{361} \times 2 \text{ millimetres}$$

=35 millimetres
Corrected winter runoff=gauged winter runoff—(+35) millimetres
=119–35 millimetres
=84 millimetres

If there is a summer rainfall 'deficit', the corrected winter runoff would be greater than the gauged winter runoff.

The corrected winter runoff of 84 millimetres is that produced by 361 millimetres of winter rainfall if 290 millimetres of rainfall had occurred in the previous summer.

2nd Adjustment

As the rainfall occurring in the driest winter in 20 years is about 70 per cent of the average winter rainfall

dry winter rainfall=70 per cent of 297 millimetres
=208 millimetres

$$\text{Estimated dry winter runoff} = \frac{\text{corrected winter}}{\text{runoff}} \times \frac{\text{dry winter rainfall}}{\text{winter rainfall}}$$

$$= 84 \times \frac{208}{361} \text{ millimetres}$$

=48 millimetres

Thus the runoff occurring in the driest winter in 20 years is estimated at 48 millimetres, but as the stream catchment area is 40 hectares the estimated total dry winter stream flow is 1920 hectare millimetres or 19 200 cubic metres, which is equivalent to an average flow throughout the winter of 1.2 litres per second.

It can be seen from the above calculations that, in this particular case, the estimated dry winter stream flow is less than half of the gauged winter stream flow, thus showing that what may appear to be an abundant source of water in some winters may well become seriously deficient in a dry winter.

Appendix H

CALCULATION OF STORAGE CAPACITY AND SOURCE SUPPLY

NETT STORAGE CAPACITY

THE following are examples of the calculation of nett capacity for the two types of storage which can be used in an irrigation scheme, viz:

    short term storage (usually 24 hours)
    winter storage

The type of storage required depends upon the quantity and reliability of the water available for supply. In each case the method of calculating the nett capacity and the source supply is illustrated. In any scheme storage calculations cannot be made until the irrigation requirements have been determined, also in the case of winter storage evaporation over the summer months and seepage losses require the provision of additional capacity over and above the nett capacity to give the actual capacity.

The graphical method of calculating storage capacity is used below in the case of short-term storage because its pictorial form helps, in some cases, to clarify the problem. If two lines are drawn on a graph to represent the cumulative or total supply and the cumulative or total demand over a period of time, the amount of nett storage capacity needed can be determined by comparing the relative positions of the lines.

SHORT-TERM STORAGE—NETT CAPACITY

A small irrigation system requires 7500 litres per hour for a period of 12 hours per day from 6 a.m. to 6 p.m. and it is assumed that the total supply equals the total demand in a 24 hour period, the variations being the periods over which the supply is available. The times when the supply is available will affect the storage capacity required. This type of storage is usually adopted when the source of water is the public mains supply, which is not sufficient to meet the peak irrigation demand either because of insufficient flow or pressure or both. Also it is sometimes used in conjunction with borehole sources.

Source supply available over the period 6 p.m. to 6 a.m.

In Fig. 12a the cumulative demand line CD has a nil value at 6 a.m., rising to a total demand of $12 \times 7500 = 90\ 000$ litres at 6 p.m.

The cumulative supply line OSD rises from a nil value at 6 p.m. to the point S at 6 a.m., when the total of 90 000 litres has been supplied. From 6 a.m. to 6 p.m. there is no supply, therefore the line is horizontal, finishing at D.

The slope of line OSD gives the required supply and the maximum amount by which the supply line rises above the demand line gives the storage capacity needed.

Thus the supply over the period 6 p.m. to 6 a.m. must be at least 7000 litres per hour, in which case a nett storage capacity of 90 000 litres will be sufficient.

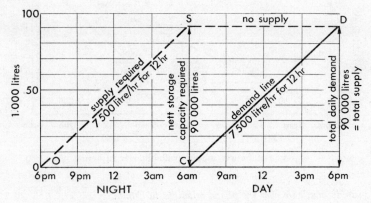

Fig. 12a. Source supply available 6 pm to 6 am

Source supply available over the period 6 p.m. to midday

In Fig. 12b the cumulative demand line CD is drawn as described above. The cumulative supply line OSD rises from a nil value at 6 p.m. to the point S at midday, when the total of 90 000 litres has been supplied. From midday to 6 p.m. there is no supply, therefore the line is horizontal, finishing at D.

In this example the supply over the period 6 p.m. to midday must be at least 5000 litres per hour, in which case a nett storage capacity of 60 000 litres will be sufficient.

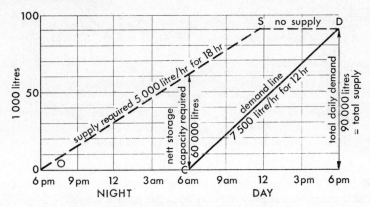

Fig. 12b. Source supply available 6 pm to midday

Source supply available over 24 hours

In Fig. 12c the cumulative demand line CD is drawn as described above. The cumulative supply line OD rises from a nil value at 6 p.m. to the point D at 6 p.m. the following day, when the total of 90 000 litres has been supplied.

In this example the supply must be at least 3750 litres per hour, in which case a nett storage capacity of 45 000 litres will be sufficient.

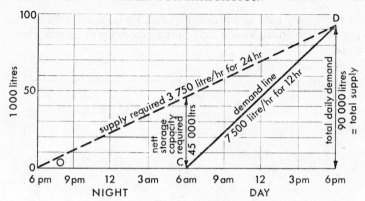

Fig. 12c. Source supply available over 24 hours

Source supply available over the period midnight to 6 p.m.

In Fig. 12d the cumulative demand line CD is drawn as described above. The cumulative supply line SD rises from a nil value at midnight to the point D at 6 p.m., when the total of 90 000 litres has been supplied.

In this example the supply over the period midnight to 6 p.m. must be at least 5000 litres per hour, in which case a storage capacity of 30 000 litres will be sufficient.

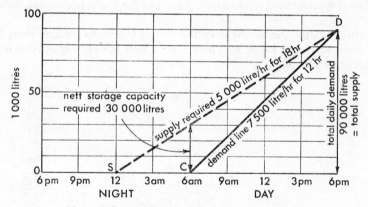

Fig. 12d. Source supply available midnight to 6 pm

Source supply of 6000 litres per hour available

In this example a supply of 6000 litres per hour is available from a source and the best method of using this supply to satisfy the demand is required.

In Fig. 12e the cumulative demand line CD is drawn as described above.

A reference line is drawn from O representing a supply of 6000 litres per hour. This is done by plotting on the graph the total supply at, say, 6 a.m., which is 12 × 6000 = 72 000 litres. CS then represents 72 000 litres and OS is the reference lines, with a slope of 6000 litres per hour.

The optimum supply is a line through D parallel to OS. Thus the graph shows that the supply of 6000 litres per hour is best taken over the period 3 a.m. to 6 p.m. in conjunction with a nett storage capacity of 18 000 litres.

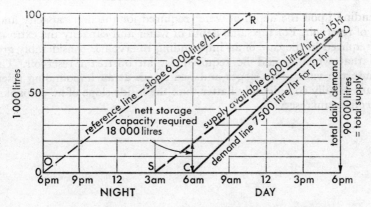

Fig. 12e. Source supply of 6000 litres per hour available

WINTER STORAGE—NETT CAPACITY

If water is abstracted from a source and stored in a reservoir during the winter months then it is necessary to store the whole of the seasonal irrigation demand that is required in the design year. In the example at Appendix A, the seasonal demand in the fifth driest year in 20 years is 16 000 m³ and nett storage is needed of at least this capacity if the seasonal demand is to be satisfied.

ALLOWANCE FOR SEEPAGE AND EVAPORATION

Additional capacity is usually required to take into account the loss of stored water due to seepage and evaporation, which is assumed to be at least 0·5 m of water depth over a 12 month period. From the point of view of short-term storage, e.g., daily storage, these losses form such a small proportion of the daily intake that they may be ignored, but in the case of winter storage they are important and should be allowed for by providing additional storage over and above that required for irrigation. The method of compensating for the losses depends upon when the water is available, viz:

(a) If sufficient additional supply is available during the irrigation season no extra storage capacity is necessary.

(b) If a supply is available only during the winter then the losses should be allowed for by extra storage capacity.

To calculate the extra storage capacity required if no additional water is available, the loss allowance of 0·5 m should be added to the depth of water required to achieve the nett capacity for a particular reservoir, and the increased depth of water is then used to calculate the actual capacity required.

WINTER STORAGE—ACTUAL CAPACITY

Thus the actual capacity is the nett capacity plus allowances for evaporation and seepage. The examples at Figs. 14 and 17 illustrate the procedure for determining the actual capacity from the nett capacity using the diagrams provided. The extra capacity required can in some cases be substantial, depending upon the depth of water required for the nett capacity and the type of reservoir. For the same depth of water and capacity the extra capacity required in the case of an impounding reservoir is considerably greater than that which would be required for an offstream reservoir. This is because the valley side slopes and bed slopes at an impounding reservoir site are usually considerably flatter than the inside slope of an embankment of an offstream reservoir.

Appendix J

WATER AUTHORITIES

INFORMATION concerning the abstraction of water for irrigation may be obtained from one of the Water Authorities listed below. Fig. 13 shows the area covered by each Authority.

ANGLIAN

Diploma House
Grammar School Walk
Huntingdon Cambs. PE18 6NZ
Tel: Huntingdon 56181

NORTHUMBRIAN

Northumbria House
Regent Centre
Gosforth
Newcastle-upon-Tyne NE3 3PX
Tel: Gosforth 843151

NORTH WEST

Dawson House
Great Sankey
Warrington WA5 3LW
Tel: Penketh 4321

SEVERN TRENT

Abelson House
2297 Coventry Road
Sheldon
Birmingham B26 3PR
Tel: Sheldon 4222

SOUTHERN

Guildbourne House
Chatsworth Road
Worthing BN11 1LD
Tel: Worthing 205252

SOUTH WEST

3–5 Barnfield Road
Exeter EX1 1RE
Tel: Exeter 50861–9

THAMES

New River Head
173 Rosebery Avenue
London EC1R 4TP
Tel: London 837 3300

WELSH NATIONAL WATER
  DEVELOPMENT AUTHORITY

Cambrian Way
Brecon
Powys LD3 7HP
Tel: Brecon 3181

77

WESSEX

Techno House
Redcliffe Way
Bristol BS1 6NY
Tel: Bristol 25491/290611

YORKSHIRE

21 Park Square South
Leeds LS1 2QG
Tel: Leeds 459404

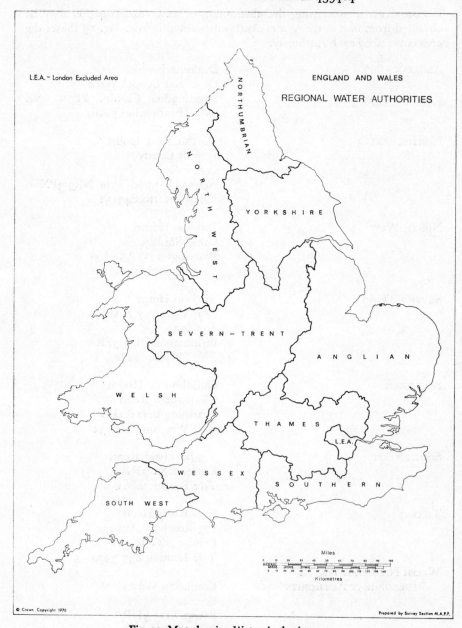

Fig. 13. Map showing Water Authority areas

Appendix K

OFFSTREAM RESERVOIRS

CAPACITY AND DEPTH OF WATER

FIG. 14 gives the depth of water in a square reservoir of given capacity and perimeter and can be used with reasonable accuracy for rectangular reservoirs with a length to width ratio of up to 1·5.

Example (see page 20):

The depth of water and capacity, after allowing for losses, are required for a reservoir having a nett capacity of 16 000 cubic metres and a perimeter of 370 metres. The 370 m point on the diagram is extended across to meet the 16 000 cubic metre point extended upwards. The point of intersection of these two lines gives the depth of water as 2·5 metres. To allow for losses in the case of winter storage the depth of water is increased by 0·5 metres to 3·0 metres and the corresponding actual capacity is found by extending the 370 m line across the diagram to meet the 3·0 metre depth of water line, which gives an actual capacity of 18 000 cubic metres.

AVERAGE DEPTH OF BALANCED EXCAVATION

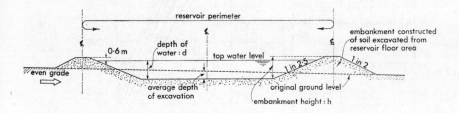

Fig. 15 gives the average depth of excavation over the reservoir floor area needed to produce sufficient soil for the embankments of square reservoirs of given perimeter and depth of water and can also be used with reasonable accuracy for rectangular reservoirs with a length to width ratio of up to 1·5.

Example (see page 20):

The average depth of excavation is required for the reservoir in the above example. The 370 m point on the diagram is extended across to meet the 3·0 metre depth of water line and the point of intersection is transferred downwards to give an average depth of excavation of 1·25 metres.

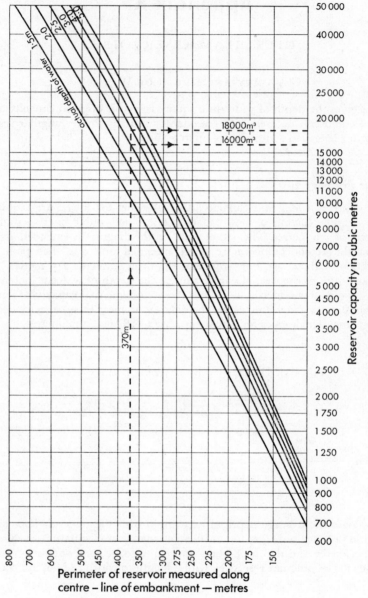

Fig. 14. Capacity and depth of water

WATER TO EARTH RATIO FOR BALANCED EXCAVATION

Fig. 16 gives the water to earth ratio of square reservoirs of given perimeter and depth of water. The diagram is reasonably accurate for rectangular reservoirs with a length to width ratio of up to 1·5.

Example (see page 21)

The water to earth ratio is required of the reservoir in the above example. The 370 m point on the diagram is extended across to meet the 3·0 metre depth of water line and the point of intersection is transferred downwards to give a water to earth ratio of 2·6.

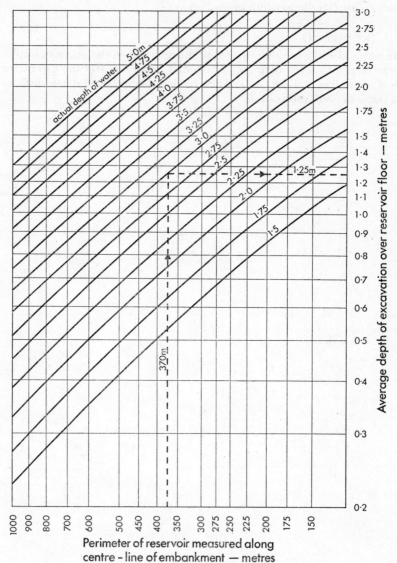

Fig. 15. Average depth of balanced excavation

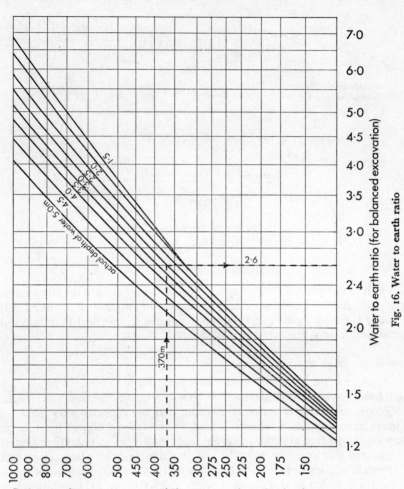

Perimeter of reservoir measured along centre-line of embankment — metres

Fig. 16. Water to earth ratio

Appendix L

IMPOUNDING RESERVOIRS

CAPACITY AND MAXIMUM DEPTH OF WATER

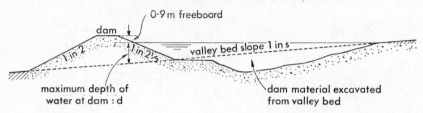

SECTION ALONG VALLEY

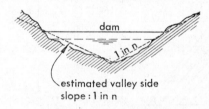

SECTION ACROSS VALLEY

Fig. 17 gives the reservoir capacity in terms of the maximum depth of water at the dam, the valley bed slope and the valley side slope. It is assumed that the valley is evenly graded and parabolic in cross section and that dam soil is excavated from within the reservoir limits.

Example (see page 26):

A reservoir of 16 000 cubic metres nett capacity is to be sited in a valley which has an average bed slope of 1 in 50 and average side slopes of 1 in 20. The maximum depth of water at the dam and the capacity after allowing for losses are required. As shown in Fig. 17 the intersection of the 1 in 20 valley side slope line and the reservoir capacity line of 16 000 cubic metres is transferred downward to meet the 1 in 50 valley bed slope line. This point of intersection gives a water depth of 3·2 metres. To take account of losses 0·5 metres is added to this depth of water to give an actual depth of water of 3·7 metres. Transferring a depth of water 3·7 metres upwards to meet the reservoir capacity lines gives an actual capacity of 25 000 cubic metres.

WATER TO EARTH RATIO

Fig. 18 gives the water to earth ratio based on the assumptions described above.

Example (see page 26):

The water to earth ratio is required for the reservoir in the above example. The 3·7 metre actual depth of water point is transferred across the diagram to meet the 1 in 50 valley bed slope line and the point of intersection is transferred downwards to give a water to earth ratio of 6·6.

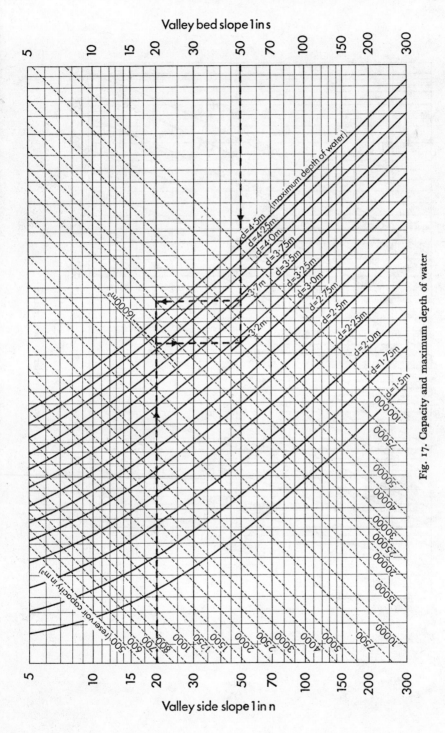

Fig. 17. Capacity and maximum depth of water

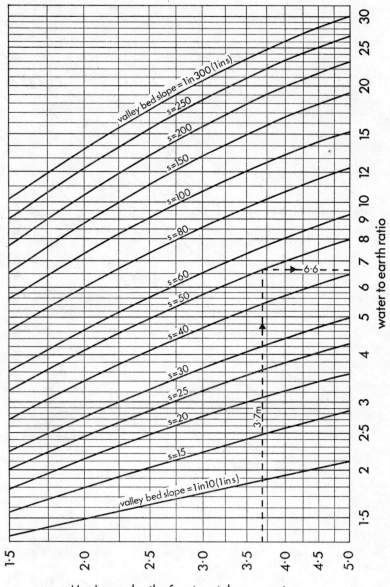

Fig. 18. Water to earth ratio

Appendix M

OFFSTREAM RESERVOIRS

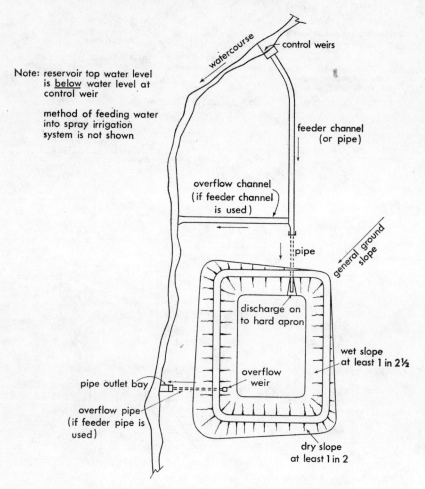

Fig. 19. General arrangement for gravity filling

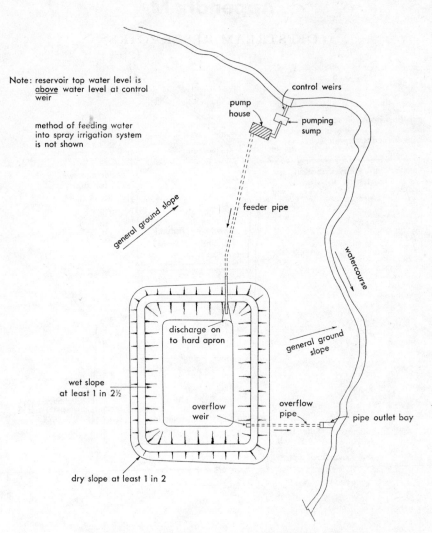

Note: reservoir top water level is <u>above</u> water level at control weir

method of feeding water into spray irrigation system is not shown

control weirs

pump house

pumping sump

general ground slope

feeder pipe

watercourse

discharge on to hard apron

wet slope at least 1 in 2½

general ground slope

overflow weir

overflow pipe

pipe outlet bay

dry slope at least 1 in 2

Fig. 20. General arrangement for pump filling

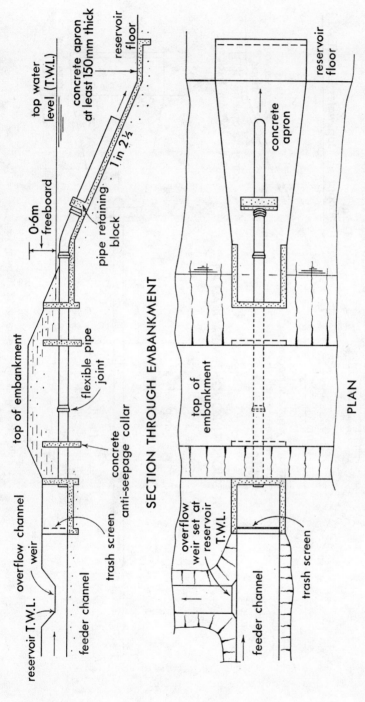

SECTION THROUGH EMBANKMENT

PLAN

Fig. 21. Typical inlet arrangement for gravity feed

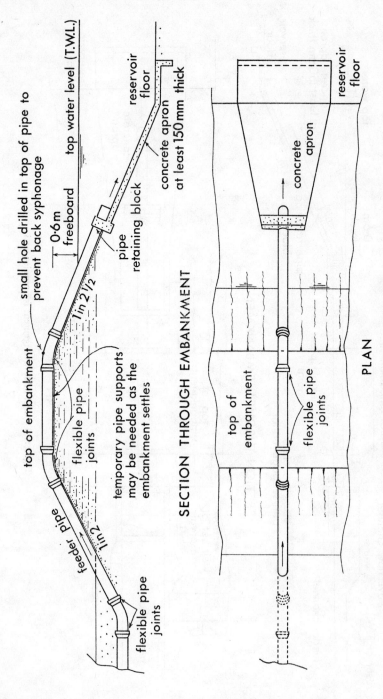

SECTION THROUGH EMBANKMENT

PLAN

Fig. 22. Typical inlet arrangement for pump feed

Appendix N

IMPOUNDING RESERVOIRS

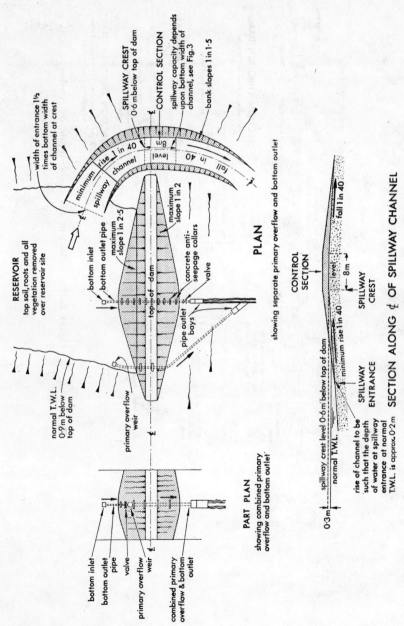

Fig. 23. Typical dam and spillway construction

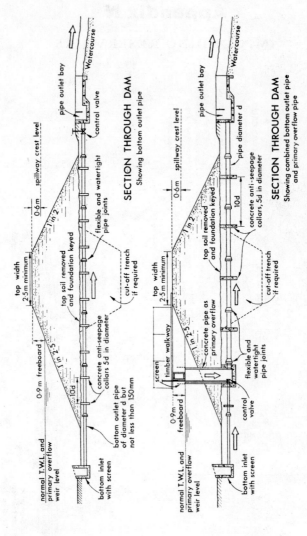

Fig. 24. Bottom outlet pipe and combined primary overflow

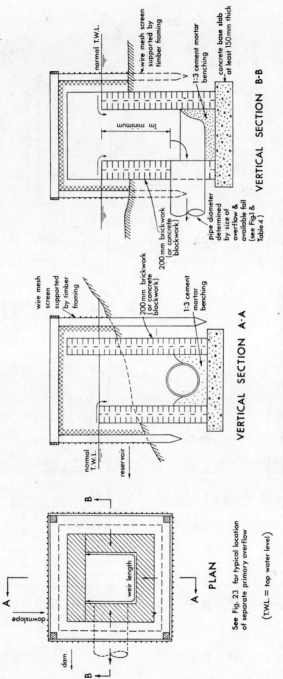

Fig. 25. Typical construction of separate primary overflow

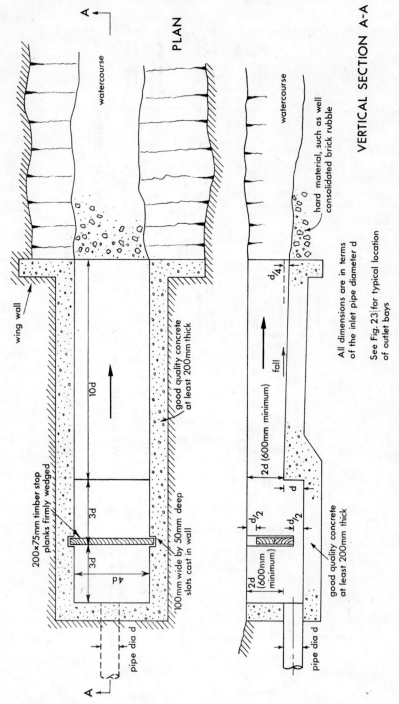

PLAN

VERTICAL SECTION A-A

wing wall

watercourse

200×75mm timber stop planks firmly wedged

100mm wide by 50mm deep slots cast in wall

good quality concrete at least 200mm thick

pipe dia d

3d

3d

4d

10d

watercourse

hard material, such as well consolidated brick rubble

All dimensions are in terms of the inlet pipe diameter d

See Fig. 23 for typical location of outlet bays

fall

d/4

2d (600mm minimum)

d

d/2

d/2

2d (600mm minimum)

2d (600mm minimum)

good quality concrete at least 200mm thick

pipe dia d

Fig. 26. Suggested design and construction of bottom outlet bay

Appendix O

REPORT ON THE YIELD TESTING OF
SEEPAGE RESERVOIRS

Name and address:..

Static water level:...............metres above/below permanent datum.

Description of permanent datum:.................................

Date	Time hours mins.	Water level metres	Pumping rate litre/second	Remarks

Notes
(1) The pumping rate, either continuous or intermittent, should be at
least equal to that required by the irrigation equipment.
(2) The water level should be recorded at regular intervals, if possible to an
accuracy of 0.01 m, and whenever the pump is stopped or restarted.
(3) On completion of the pump yield test, the water level should be recorded
at regular intervals until it has reached its maximum recovery.
(4) If the depression of the water level on pumping is small compared to the
available depth of water and if the recovery of the water level on
completion of pumping is rapid, then the reservoir could be expected to
provide an adequate supply.
(5) Prior authority for pump testing a seepage reservoir should be obtained
from the Water Authority.

Appendix P

METRIC UNITS

length: 1 metre (m) =1000 millimetres (mm)
area: 1 hectare (ha) =10 000 square metres (m²)
volume: 1 cubic metre (m³) =1000 litres (litre)
   1 hectare millimetre (ha mm) =10 cubic metres (m³)
flow: 1 litre per second (litre/s)   =3·6 cubic metres per hour (m³/h)
   =8·6 hectare millimetre per day (ha mm/day)
application
rate: 1 mm/hour (mm/h) on 1 hectare (ha) =10 cubic metres per hour (m³/h)
power: 1 kilowatt (kW)   =2·8 litre/sec (litre/s)

APPROXIMATE CONVERSIONS

(Accuracy to within 3 per cent)

1 foot   =0·3 metres
1 inch   =25 millimetres
1 acre   =0·4 hectares
1 cubic yard=0·75 cubic metres
1 million gallons=4500 cubic metres
1 acre inch=10 hectare millimetres
1 cubic foot per second (cusec) =28 litres per second
1 horsepower=0·75 kilowatts
1 cubic metre=220 gallons
1 cubic metre per second (cumec) =35 cubic feet per second (cusec)

Index

Abstraction licences, 7
Accessibility, reservoir site, 16, 17
Additional water supply, 15, 75
Allowance for embankment settlement, 44
                seepage and evaporation,
                15, 75
Application, rate of water, 3, 53
Anti-seepage collars, 37, 47, 89, 92
Asbestos cement pipes, 46
Average depth of balanced excavation, 20, 79
Aquifers, 11

Bacteriological quality of water, 6, 60
Balanced excavation, average depth, 20, 79
Bentonite, 37, 40, 51
Blanket construction, 40
Bottom outlet bay, 34, 94
              pipe, 29, 33, 37, 92
Borehole pump, cost, 61
Boreholes, cost, 61
        depth, 11, 12
        diameter, 11, 12
        yield testing, 11, 12
Butyl rubber lining, 33, 40, 50, 51
Bypass channel, 13

Calculation of water requirements, 3, 4, 5, 52
              source supply, 72 et seq.
Calculation of storage capacity, 72 et seq.
Capacity, actual storage, 15, 20, 25, 74, 79, 84
        extra storage, 75
        nett storage, 15, 20, 25, 72 et seq. 79, 84
        short-term storage, 15, 76
        winter storage, 20, 25, 76
Cast iron pipes, 46
Catchment runoff, 10
Central Water Planning Unit, 11
Channel, bypass, 13
        feeder, 16, 21, 87
        spillway, 17, 30, 32, 91
Chemical quality of water, 6, 59
Clay lining, 40, 50
        pits, 14
        soils, 17, 36 et seq.
Collars, anti-seepage, 37, 47, 89, 92
Consolidation, embankment, 44
Construction, embankment, 44
Control section, spillway, 30, 32, 91

Control weirs, stream, 25
Costs, boreholes, 61
        earth reservoirs, 61
        pumping, 22, 62
        waterproofing, 51
Crops, high value, 4
        low value, 5
Cumulative demand, 72 et seq.
Cut-off trench, 37, 41, 42, 43, 51

Daily demand, 3, 53, 72 et seq.
Dams, earth, see earth embankments
Demand, cumulative, 72 et seq.
        daily, 3, 53, 72 et seq.
        hourly, 3, 53
        seasonal, 3, 53
Depth, average balanced excavation, 20, 79
Depth of water, 17, 20, 24, 79, 84
        maximum, 24, 84
Design storm flows, 26 et seq.
Design year, 4
Diaphragm construction, 40, 43
Direct abstraction, 6
Drains, field, 19
Draw-down effect, 40
Dry winter stream flow, 8, 9, 10, 68, 70

Earth dams, see earth embankments
Earth embankments, blanket construction, 40, 43
        consolidation, 44
        construction, 44
        core, 40, 43
        diaphragm construction, 40, 43
        grassing, 45
        homogeneous construction, 40, 41
        maintenance, 47
        pipework, 45, 46
        protection, 45
        seepage, 36, 37
Earth embankments, settlement, 44
        sliding, 36
        slopes, 44
        stability, 44
        suitable soils, 38
        top width, 44
        waterproofing, 40, 48 et seq.
        zoned construction, 40, 48

Erosion, embankment protection, 36, 38, 45
        feeder channel protection, 21
        internal, 36
        spillway protection, 33
        surface, 36
Evaporation allowance, 15, 75
Excavation, balanced, average depth, 20, 81
        slopes, 44
Extra storage capacity, 75

Feeder channel, 21
                maximum slopes, 21
                maximum velocities, 21
Feeder pipe, 21, 87
Field drainage water, 11, 13
Field drains, 19
Flood flows, see storm flows
Flow gauges, readings, 10, 68
                rectangular notch, 10, 66
                vee notch, 10, 64
Flow gauging, 10
Foundations, rock, 36
        seepage control, 37
        site preparation, 37
        stability, 36
        suitable soils, 38
Freeboard, reservoir, 20, 26
Friction losses, pipe, 23

Gauge, rectangular weir, 10, 66
        vee notch, 10, 64
Grant aid, 61
Gravel pits, 14
Gravity supply, 16, 21, 87
Ground water, 11, 14, 34

Holes, trial, 18
Homogeneous construction, 40, 41
Hourly demand, 3, 53

Impermeable soils, 16, 17, 36 et seq.
Impounding licences, 8
Impounding reservoirs, 17, 25 et seq., 84, 91
        capacity, 25, 74, 84
        dimensions, 25, 74,
                84
        freeboard, 26, 84
        maximum depth of
                water, 26, 84
        overflow design,
                27, 91 et seq.
        overflows, 26
Impounding reservoirs, primary overflow,
                27, 91 et seq.
        spillway, 18, 30,
                91 et seq.
        valley bed slopes,
                18, 26, 84, 85
        valley side slopes,
                18, 26, 84, 85
        water to earth
                ratio, 18, 26, 84, 85

Joints, pipe, 45

Licences, abstraction, 7
        impounding, 8
Linings reservoir, butyl rubber, 48, 49, 50
        clay, 50
        fixing, 48, 49
        laying, 48, 49
        polyethylene, 48, 49, 50
        PVC, 48, 49, 50
        soil cover, 49
Location, reservoir, 16, 17
        spillway, 18
Losses, evaporation, 15, 75
        seepage, 15, 75
        storage, 15, 75

Maintenance, 47
Maximum depth of water, 24, 84
Maximum slopes, embankments (and
                dams), 44
        excavations, 44
        feeder channel, 21
Maximum slopes, spillway, 30
Maximum velocities, feeder channel, 21
        spillway, 33
Metric units, 96

Nett storage capacity, 15, 20, 25, 72 et
        seq., 79, 84

Offstream reservoirs, 16, 20 et seq., 79, 87, 88
        capacity, 20, 79
        delivery, pumped, 22,
                88
        depth of excavation,
                17, 20, 79
        depth of water, 17,
                20, 79
        dimensions, 17, 20, 79
        feeder channel, 21, 87
        feeder pipe, 21, 87
        freeboard, 20
        gravity feed, 16, 21, 87
        overflows, 24, 87, 88
        perimeter, 20, 79
        pump feed, 22, 88
        water to earth ratio,
                17, 20, 79
Overflow pipe, dimensions, 24, 27, 28
        location, 24, 87, 88, 91
        outlet weir, 27, 93
        slopes, 28
Overflows, offstream reservoir, 24, 87, 88
        impounding reservoir, 26, 91

Perimeter, offstream reservoir, 20, 79
Permeable soil, 36 et seq., 48
Pipe, bottom outlet, 29, 33, 37, 92
        feeder, 21, 87
        overflow, 24, 27, 28, 87, 88, 91, 93
        pump delivery, 22, 88

Pipes, asbestos cement, 46
    cast iron, 46
    concrete, 46
    polyethylene, 46
    PVC, 46
    spun iron, 46
    steel, 46
Pipework, reservoir, 45
Piping, embankments, 36
Pipes, friction losses, 23
Polyethylene lining, 48, 49, 50
Potential transpiration, 3
Primary overflow capacity, 27
Primary overflow pipe, dimensions, 28
        location, 27, 91
        outlet weir, 29, 93
        slopes, 28
        type, 29, 92
Public supply, 12
Pump, delivery pipe, 23, 24, 88
    selection, 22
    suction, 22
Pumping costs, 22, 62
    sump, 24
PVC pipes, 46
    lining, 48, 49, 50

Quality of water, 6, 59, 60
Quantity of water, 6

Rainfall, percolation, 34
Rectangular weir flow gauge, 10, 66
Residual flow, 8, 9
Reservoir capacity, 20, 25, 74, 79, 84
    dimensions, 17, 20, 25, 74, 79, 84
    perimeter, 20, 79
    waterproofing, see lining
    and waterproofing
Reservoir site, accessibility, 16, 17
        location, 16, 17
        preparation, 37
        selection, 16 et seq.
        vegetation removal, 37, 48
        watertightness, 16, 17
Reservoirs Act 1976, 1
Reservoirs, impounding, 17, 25 et seq., 84, 91
    offstream, 16, 20 et seq., 79, 87, 88
    seepage, 34
    Safety Provisions Act 1930, 1
Restriction on spray irrigation, 9
Rubber, butyl lining, 48, 49, 50
Runoff, estimation, 9, 10
    catchment, 9, 10, 30

Seasonal demand, 3, 53
Seepage, allowance, 15, 75
    control, 37
Seepage, paths, 38
    through embankments, 36, 37
    through foundations, 37

Seepage reservoirs, 34
        yield testing, 35
Settlement, embankment, 44
Short-term storage, 15, 74
Site, reservoir, see reservoir site
Slopes, embankments (and dams), 44
    excavations, 44
Soil proportions, 38
Soil testing, 38, 39
Soil moisture deficit, 3, 4, 5
Soils, clay, 17, 36 et seq.
    impermeable, 16, 17, 36 et seq.
    permeable, 36 et seq., 48
Spun iron pipes, 46
Spillway capacity, 30, 31, 32
    channel, 17, 30, 32, 91
    control section, 30, 32, 91
    crest, 30, 91
    curtailment, 18, 88
    design, 30, 31, 32, 88
    entrance, 30, 88
    erosion protection, 33
    grassing, 33
    location, 18
    maximum velocity, 33
    slopes, 30
Stability of embankments, 44
    foundations, 36
Steel pipes, 46
Storage,
    actual capacity, 15, 20, 25, 76, 84
    extra capacity, 75, 76
    field drainage water, 11, 13
    ground water, 14, 34
    losses, 15
    nett capacity, 15, 20, 25, 75, 84
    short-term, 15, 74
    surface water, 13
    winter, 15, 20, 26, 75
Storm overflow, see spillway
Streams, control weirs, 25
    flow gauging, 10
    stability, 18
Stream flow, dry winter, 8, 9, 10, 68, 70
    estimating, 10, 68, 70
Supply, additional, 15, 75
    gravity, 16, 21, 87
    pumped, 22, 88
    winter, 72
Surface water, 8, 13

Testing, soil, 38, 39
Testing, yield, boreholes, 11, 12
    seepage reservoirs, 35
Top widths, embankment (and dams), 44
Transpiration, potential, 3
Trench, cut-off, 37, 41, 42, 43, 51
Trial holes, cost, 18
    position, 18

Underground water, occurrence, 10, 34
    abstraction, 11, 34

Valley bed slopes, 18, 26, 84, 85
        side slopes, 18, 26, 84, 85
Vee notch flow gauge, 10, 64

Water, additional supply, 15, 75
        cost, 7
        public supply, 12
        quality, bacteriological, 6, 60
               chemical, 6, 59
        quantity, 6
        surface, 8, 13
        underground, 10, 11, 34
Water Authorities, 7, 8, 77
Water Resources Act 1963, 1, 7
Water to earth ratio, 17, 18, 20, 26, 79,
                84, 86

Waterproofing, 48 *et seq.*
        costs, 51
        cut-off, 37, 41, 42, 43, 51
        sheet lining, 48, 49, 50
        soil treatment, 50, 51
Weed-killer, 48, 49
Weir, rectangular flow gauge, 10, 66
        stream control, 25
Well points, 11
Wells, 11, 34
Winter runoff examples, 10
        storage, 15, 20, 26, 75

Yield testing, boreholes, 11, 12
        seepage reservoirs, 35

Zoned embankment construction, 40, 42

Printed in England for Her Majesty's Stationery Office by Headley Brothers Ltd
109 Kingsway London WC2B 6PX and Ashford Kent

Dd 497399 K24 4/77